Resource Management
in the NHS

# Health Services Management Series

Health care has become a major issue for western governments. It commands a significant proportion of national wealth, and rising professional and public expectations threaten to increase it yet further. There is a seemingly insatiable demand for additional resources, usually in excess of the general rise in prosperity. Consequently, cost containment has been much in vogue in recent years, finding expression in such policies as priority for lower cost primary medical care.

In the British National Health Service, as in many other countries, market disciplines are largely muted or absent. There are few competitive pressures and thereby incentive for health authorities, hospitals, clinics or professionals to promote efficiency. The alternative in the NHS has been cash-limited financial allocations to health authorities and, more recently, government insistence on cash-releasing 'cost-improvements'.

There has also been increasing attention to NHS management. It is seen as a much more important factor in performance than was the case in the early years of the service. Administrators, for example, were seen mainly as supportive, ensuring systems ran smoothly for professionals who led the development of the service. The idea of managers as a much more positive force responsible for planning and directing development only began to take root in the 1970s, culminating in the appointment of general managers in 1984–6.

Expectations of managers will continue to accelerate, given their higher profile in the organization. The management of NHS resources will become even more challenging since the gap between what is affordable (under any system) and professional and public aspirations is likely to continue to grow. Pressures to improve efficiency will intensify, along with those to ensure that services are more sensitive to the wishes of consumers. Managers will also have to be more rigorous in their examination of the benefits of developments, particularly those utilizing expensive technology.

The rapid development of the role of NHS managers has outstripped the capacity of training institutions and schools of management to respond to their needs. There are relatively few texts which relate management theories and skills to the circumstances of publicly-provided health care. The answer is not to be found in an uncritical transfer of private-sector techniques. A good example is the relative failure of the first four 'demonstration' projects, seeking to introduce clinical management budgeting for acute services.

This series of books is intended to make good a little of the deficiency in suitable educational and training materials, necessary to underpin the development of management. The aim will be to relate advances in theories, systems, techniques and skills to the management of health care organizations, particularly the NHS. The books will be primarily concerned with practical problems and issues of concern to those involved in the management, not just managers.

Health Services Management Series
Series Editor Stuart Haywood

# Resource Management in the NHS

## JOHN PERRIN

Visiting Lecturer, Health Services Management
  Centre, University of Birmingham
Price Waterhouse Fellow in Public Sector
  Accounting, University of Exeter
Emeritus Professor, University of Warwick

**CHAPMAN & HALL**
London · Glasgow · New York · Tokyo · Melbourne · Madras

In association with Health Services Management Centre

**Published by Chapman & Hall, 2-6 Boundary Row, London SE1 8HN**

Chapman & Hall, 2-6 Boundary Row, London SE1 8HN, UK

Blackie Academic & Professional, Wester Cleddens Road, Bishopbriggs, Glasgow G64 2NZ, UK

Chapman & Hall, 29 West 35th Street, New York NY10001, USA

Chapman & Hall Japan, Thomson Publishing Japan, Hirakawacho Nemoto Building, 6F, 1-7-11 Hirakawa-cho, Chiyoda-ku, Tokyo 102, Japan

Chapman & Hall Australia, Thomas Nelson Australia, 102 Dodds Street, South Melbourne, Victoria 3205, Australia

Chapman & Hall India, R. Seshadri, 32 Second Main Road, CIT East, Madras 600 035, India

First edition 1988
Reprinted 1990, 1991, 1992

© 1988 John Perrin

Printed in Great Britain by TJ Press Ltd, Padstow, Cornwall

ISBN 0 412 37550 8

A catalogue record for this book is available from the British Library

# Contents

# Series editor's preface

A book on resource management seems an appropriate way to start the series. Managers have been much pre-occupied with financial issues in recent years. Problems of financial control, particularly in acute hospitals, and initiatives to find additional cash from improvements in efficiency have featured prominently in the agendas of health authorities. Yet managers continue to be handicapped by inadequate financial information which is unable to sustain, for example, financial allocations to budget holders related to workloads. At the same time there has been a rapid acceleration in the capacity of financial systems, facilitated by computer technology. In these circumstances there is pressure to move very quickly and in so doing make mistakes. The first round of relatively expensive projects to develop budgets for clinicians were undermined, in John Perrin's view, by an underestimation of likely difficulties. In contrast, he feels that the new information systems, which take account of developments elsewhere while reflecting the circumstances and objectives of NHS personnel will be implemented, albeit gradually and grudgingly.

The book provides an overview of current developments in financial management and assesses their potential. It draws on John Perrin's considerable financial expertise and experience of the NHS, supplemented by a review of the field made possible with financial help from the secretariat of the NHS/DHSS Steering Group on Health Service Information. The aim is to help managers, health authorities and others with a practical interest in the better use of NHS resources to make more informed judgements on the development of financial systems for their organization.

John Perrin also looks forward to the likely pattern of development. It is a challenging scenario which will have an impact well beyond the world of finance departments. The implications of new costing and then budgetary systems for professionals, particularly doctors, is already widely recognized. It will open some of their decisions to wider scrutiny, probably leading to a redefinition of clinical freedom. There are also far-reaching implications for the job content of managers (in the broadest sense). It remains to be seen how directors of finance and general managers will respond to a situation in which their responsibility for the level of service in a particular specialty is much clearer than it is at present. John Perrin is right to point to the need for more investment in training to prepare staff for the considerable changes in prospect.

Another reason to welcome the book is its interest in improving health care. The primary requirement of new costing and budgetary systems is that they contribute to the development of high-quality services by improving management. John Perrin's book should help the NHS meet that requirement, since it is not about improving financial management for its own sake. It is about the development of appropriate systems to inform allocations and use of scarce resources.

Stuart Haywood
Health Services Management Centre
University of Birmingham

# CHAPTER 1
# Introduction

**1.1**   This book is written for the interest and use of all who are decision-makers in the National Health Service: health authority chairpersons and members, general managers and other senior officers, clinicians, and managers at every level and in every profession. It is *not* a how-to-do-it manual or textbook of NHS accountancy or financial information systems. It *is* an attempt to explain the types of costing, budgetary and other financial information already available, or likely to become available in the near future, for the assistance of planning, management and performance review in the National Health Service (NHS). The book seeks to minimize technical jargon, but some jargon, or technical terminology, is inevitable. This is defined or explained when technical terms are first used in chapters, and it is summarized in the very extensive glossary included at the back of the book.

**1.2**   The glossary is intended to be a distinctive feature of this book – it may be used independently of the chapters by those readers who need quick access to specific definitions and guidance on reference reading. Indeed, the chapters have been kept largely free of many source reference citations or bibliographical suggestions, so that readers will not be distracted from the general flow of understanding of NHS financial information, and its uses.

## The need for better financial information and management

**1.3**   The potential for increasing both the volume and the quality of health services – preventive, curative and caring – seems unlimited. The available resources, which essentially means the available finance provided by governments to buy resources, are obviously not unlimited. There may indeed be a good case for increasing spending on health services. But that is not the subject of this book. The subject of this book is the use of financial information to maximize the benefit or contribution the NHS can make to society. Some may think of this as maximizing 'value for money' for the tax-payers' funds expended in the NHS. Others may think of it as simply maximizing the output of caring service. Whichever way you think of it, the author assumes readers will agree that NHS management and management information systems should be devoted to producing the best possible outcomes for patients, both individually and collectively. With the relentless increase in the number in need, the range of treatments possible, and the sophistication and costliness of many treatments, the problem of tight resources is steadily becoming more severe. And thus it becomes every decision-maker's business to be very conscious of what things cost, and how to budget. 'What things cost' is simple to say, but often difficult to measure let alone control.

**1.4**   In her Preface to the Sixth Report of the NHS/DHSS Health Services Information Steering Group (see under 'Körner' in the Glossary for full bibliographic documentation), Mrs Edith Körner wrote that 'The management of the NHS must at all times be able to demonstrate that the very large amount of public expenditure devoted to health care is properly spent, that funds are prudently allocated, expenditure strictly controlled, performance critically examined and competing claims for resources judiciously assessed.'

**1.5**   The Sixth Report states (paragraph 1.11) that:

'The financial analysis required to plan and to manage the provision and delivery of health services must answer the questions:

(a)   *What* is the money spent on?
(b)   *Who* spends the money?
(c)   *Where* is the money spent?
(d)   *Why* is it spent?'

Naturally, the NHS has had cost and budgetary systems since its earliest days, but unfortunately they have not been at all good at answering these questions. They were designed primarily to ensure probity, to control *total* expenditure and to provide data to the DHSS, rather than to assist management.

**1.6**   The picture is now set to change. Newly devised cost accounting and budgeting systems, designed first and foremost as tools of management, will provide the means to answer the first three of these questions and are beginning to get to grips with the fourth. And once they can be linked with improved information systems covering health services activities and manpower it should become possible:

a   To *distinguish* precisely what has taken place, and at what cost;
b   To *forecast* what is likely to happen, and how much it is likely to cost;
c   To *introduce deliberate changes* in the pattern of health care provision, knowing what the effects of such changes are likely to be;
d   To *provide staff with budgets*, based on defined levels of activity, which they can positively control.

## Background and acknowledgements

**1.7**   This book is a long-delayed consequence of awareness at the

NHS/DHSS Steering Group on Health Services Information that there were research and systems developments in NHS costing and budgeting which were possibly outside the Steering Group's brief, yet of sufficient importance to be linked with the introduction and progress of new initiatives contained in their Sixth Report. Indeed, there are an enormous number of such financial information systems developments going on throughout the country, and this author cannot begin to mention them all individually.

The good news is that many of these new development seem likely to improve substantially the quality of local management control and planning information. The bad news is that there is so much local initiative going on – with different systems specifications, different software, different hardware (i.e. computer hardware), and different reporting systems – that almost certainly a considerable waste of public money is being experienced.

More centrally to the objective of this book, the concern is that much cost and budgeting information will be produced that is based on such different criteria or specifications that it cannot meaningfully be used in inter-district performance comparisons. The delay in the appearance of this book is a result of 'overload' brought about by the amount of information being produced in the NHS on financial information systems developments. The amount of paper collected by the author during the drafting of this book makes a stack six feet high!

1.8   The author is grateful to acknowledge Alastair Mason (formerly of the Körner Steering Group) and Stuart Haywood (of the Health Services Management Centre, Birmingham) as the sources of conception of this book. Also from Birmingham, Christopher Day and Tony Cook have been most helpful in contributing comment, criticism, and opportunities to meet literally hundreds of NHS financial, clinical and other professional staff on courses and seminars where NHS financial problems could be opened up to rational debate. Thanks go also to Ray Hillman and Iden Wickings, in particular but among many other NHS treasurers and researchers, for helpful comments and willingness to allow publication of research materials. David Poynton and Chris Savory also were most helpful. But I can end only by mentioning the debt of all of us to Edith Körner for providing the dynamic which allowed so many of the recent NHS management information innovations to take root.

1.9   In passing, please note that in this book the old-fashioned, traditional title of 'treasurer' is used to denote the chief financial officer (CFO) of a health authority. Since the 1982 reorganization, and especially the Griffiths Inquiry recommendations towards a more business orientated management organization structure in the NHS, a variety of titles have crept into use for the CFO. Also the CFO's duties have frequently been expanded to include management information, computing, 'resources', and bits of administration which the new general managers did not want to have to deal with in person. I have kept to the title of treasurer because whatever additional duties may be 'tacked on' to the CFO's function, the only main responsibility for which the CFO is legally and ethically accountable is to ensure that the health authority's money has been expended and accounted for under the law of the land.

## Structure of the book

**1.10**  Chapter 2 provides background on the need for improved financial information and performance in the NHS, and it explains the nature and importance of the separate concepts of *economy, efficiency* and *effectiveness.* Chapter 3 explains the main cost concepts and measures relevant to management in the NHS, and Chapter 4 discusses the problems and features of effective budgetary planning and control. Chapter 5 considers the Körner initiatives for improved health services financial information, and the use of functional management budgeting by unit management.

**1.11**  The remaining chapters relate to newer developments not yet in general use in the NHS, but which offer promise for assisting better management of NHS resources in future years. Chapter 6 introduces specialty costing, after Magee and Körner. Specialty costing is an essential stepping stone of development to budgeting for specialties or individual clinicians, so Chapter 7 is devoted to clinical management budgets. Chapter 8 discusses resource management – a concept wider than budgeting and current cost control, to include using cost and other resource information in the decision-making of clinicians and other resource managers – as well as the provision of option appraisal and information on the cost of use of capital assets. Chapter 9 looks forward to patient costing, and to case-mix costing and budgeting (including the use of DRGs, or diagnosis related groups). Chapter 10 presents the author's conclusions on what the NHS should aim to achieve within the next ten years in the provision of financial information and its use by clinical and other management. There then follows the very extensive Glossary, which additionally contains many bibliographical citations for further reading on specialized topics of interest to readers.

## Summary

1 This book was written for health authority members, general managers, clinicians, senior nurses and members of other health professions. It may also prove useful to trainees in management and finance.

2 The book assumes its readers have no prior training in, or formal knowledge of, accountancy and finance.

3 A large glossary is to be found at the back of the book. This can be used independently from the main text for quick reference to technical terminology.

4 This book does not seek to make any economic or political judgement on what level of funding or resources should be available to the NHS. But regardless of whether resources seem generous or inadequate, there is an ethical obligation upon all health authority members and employees to make the best possible use of all available resources.

5 Clinicians largely determine the NHS workload and pressure on resources, at least in hospitals. They must take a share in using financial and workload information to help improve hospital performance in the interest of patients. For each professional group the management control information provided must be relevant, and the form or degree of involvement in costing or budgeting must be appropriate to the responsibilities held.

6 The book was inspired by the Körner programme. The Körner programme was primarily concerned with improvements to NHS management information which could be attained quickly, cheaply and universally throughout the service. However, the book goes beyond Körner to consider further financial information developments which pioneering districts can attempt now, as 'resource management' projects.

7 The first two chapters of the book give background. The next three chapters explain the 'state of the art' of the NHS costing and budgeting up to Körner. Chapter 6 introduces the Körner initiative of 'specialty costing'. Chapter 7 introduces the Griffiths initiative of 'clinical management budgeting'. Chapter 8 discusses the post-Griffiths initiative of 'resource management' projects. The final two chapters look to further developments which could arise experimentally in some resource management projects but are likely to take ten years or more to enter universal use throughout the NHS.

# CHAPTER 2
# Economy, efficiency and effectiveness

## Background

**2.1** *Health Care and Its Costs*, published in 1983 by the Department of Health and Social Security (DHSS), provided a useful background and insight into the patterns of funding, staffing and activity (i.e. the health care services provided) for the NHS in England over the decade from 1971 to 1981. Whilst some have criticized this publication as a public relations exercise more concerned with the volume of health care than with its quality, it does illustrate (p. 6) that funding and manpower (even after adjustment for the effects of the 1974 reorganization and for shorter working weeks introduced in later years) rose between 1971 and 1976 by more than twice the rise in the major indicators of activity (or 'output') over that period.

In contrast, this relationship was reversed between 1976 and 1981. Thus, even while granting that the statistics of activity cited are measures of 'health care workload' rather than the more important but as yet largely unavailable measures of 'health care outcomes', the figures do seem to show that 'productivity' in the Hospital and Community Health Services fell from 1971 to 1976, but rose from 1976 to 1981. A further rise in 'productivity' appears to be illustrated in the DHSS's Annual Report 1984, *The Health Service in England*, for the years 1982 and 1983.

Of course, many of the 'productivity' statistics relate to numbers of cases handled. The higher 'productivity' largely derives from shorter length of stay (LOS) for most hospital inpatients. Shorter LOS can result from technological improvements (in drugs, surgery, therapy, etc.) or from consultants, under pressure to find beds for new admissions, discharging patients earlier than their medical or social circumstances would ideally justify. Some patients in this latter category may have to be seen again to remedy the consequences of early discharge: unfortunately we do not know their number, but they add to the workload/output statistics and thus the apparent evidence of higher productivity, whereas any meaningful measurement of 'outcomes', or quality of care, would show a fall if there are avoidable re-admissions.

Against that, where there are long waiting lists of patients needing care, it is certainly possible that the 'greatest good for the greatest number' will be attained by shortening LOS if this means that a greater number of patients can be treated with less delay. Under constrained resources, it is a problem of deciding the 'trade-off' between quality of care for each *individual* patient already under treatment, and the social benefit of treating a larger number of patients in need of care at a lower level of thoroughness. This is not a choice which the caring professions would wish to have to make, but it may be an inevitable choice if overall NHS resources are inadequate to meet all need at a high standard of quality.

At the same time, it is an easy platitude to state that resources are inadequate: governments may insist on evidence that need cannot be met from existing resources. This evidence depends upon information regarding the economy, efficiency and effectiveness with which existing health care resources are being used. The NHS has a poor record in providing such evidence. Hence the need for better information systems to demonstrate the evidence where performance is good, or to provoke reform and improvement where performance is not yet good.

**2.2** On recent central government funding policies the NHS Hospital and Community Services must plan on 'level funding' – that is, a level or stable volume of resources after allowing for inflation. On recent evidence, growth money allocated is likely to be needed largely to meet government under funding of allowed pay awards. And of course this 'level funding' generalization ignores the complications that:

a   on the DHSS's own previous estimates there needs to be growth in funding of about 0.7% per annum to keep pace with the ageing population, plus about 0.5% for medical/technological innovation; and that

b   the working of the formula of the Resources Allocation Working Party (RAWP), which aims to equalize standards and access to good acute health care locally throughout the country, operates so that in a state of 'level funding' the equalization process inevitably involves the contraction of funding in well provided districts in order to fund limited RAWP growth elsewhere.

On present trends and after allowing for (a) above, very few health districts gaining under RAWP reallocation will actually have any genuine growth money for new developments, unless they can save it elsewhere. For health districts losing under RAWP, mainly in central London and other inner city areas – and often teaching districts with famous hospitals – contraction is inevitable on present funding policies. The management of the contracting health districts are involved in a process of 'damage limitation'. Though the latter case is the more severe, in fact nearly all health districts are now under extreme financial pressure if the needs and potential for really good health care are to be met. Thus all health districts and their budget holders and other managers – and all their staff in the caring professions – must take an increasing interest, and direct involvement, in local issues promoting economy, efficiency and effectiveness.

**2.3** The Royal Commission on the NHS a decade ago reported on a broad front regarding the improvements needed in the NHS. The Commission's main concern was with the quality and range of services requiring further

development. But the Royal Commission did additionally recognize that
with resources being limited relative to needs at any given point in time, it
was important to improve management information and financial control.
The Royal Commission's main report did not go into much detail, but in
general it commended to the NHS that attention should be given to the 56
comments and recommendations contained in its Research Paper No. 2,
*Management of Financial Resources in the National Health Service.*

Apparently the DHSS was sympathetic to many of the recommendations,
since several research and development grants for the improvement of NHS
financial and other management information were awarded within the
next few years. The most important of these grants was to establish the
NHS/DHSS Health Services Information Steering Group, whose reports
came to be known as the Körner Reports in recognition of the eminent
leadership of the Steering Group by its chairperson, Mrs Edith Körner.

The terms of reference of the Health Services Information Steering Group
were set out in its *First Report to the Secretary of State*:

1  to agree, implement and keep under review principles and procedures to
   guide the future development of health services information systems;
2  to identify and resolve health service information issues requiring a co-
   ordinated approach;
3  to review existing health services information systems; and
4  to consider proposals for changes to, or developments in, health services
   information systems arising elsewhere and, if acceptable, to assess priorities
   for their development and implementation.

**2.4**   Much of the work of the Steering Group was progressed through
working groups concentrating on hospital and community activity, on manpower and on financial information. All three areas were seen as inter-
linking and needing to progress in parallel so that they may be drawn upon
simultaneously for purpose of performance assessment and control.

Although most of their work focused on the better monitoring and control
of NHS operations, this implicitly also assumed effective feedback into
operational planning. Their work include the derivation of 'minimum data
sets' to provide essential information for management monitoring and
control. The minimum data sets specify the minimum data which *all* health
districts should have available, and which regions and the DHSS may need
to receive in routine reporting. However, nothing in the minimum-data-set
approach is intended to prevent or inhibit individual health authorities
from developing additional information which local management finds
useful in improving the quality of planning, decision-making and control.

## Economy, efficiency and effectiveness

**2.5**   The need for better financial information has been known to
treasurers for a long time and was brought to wider attention in Research
Paper No. 2 for the Royal Commission on the NHS. Many treasurers have
done their best, but there have been shortages of sufficient posts graded
highly enough to attract and retain skilled staff in the face of competition
from other employers, together with constraints imposed by management

cost controls and difficulties until now in securing local district access to adequate computing power in the light of DHSS policy to concentrate NHS computing in regional mainframes.

Finally, neither treasurers nor any other single officer or manager have been able to ensure that progress in the separate financial, activity and manpower information systems moves forward at the same pace, on a planned basis of interlinked compatibility and relevance. However, given the financial squeeze on NHS growth money and the actual contraction of services in some districts, the considerable change in attitudes manifested, for example, in the widespread interest and support for the Körner Steering Group's initiatives, and finally the explosion of economical micro computing power now available for use in all disciplines, the scene would appear to be set for rapid progress in information systems developments helpful to operational efficiency and effectiveness.

**2.6** VFM stands for 'value-for-money', and the concept represents the concern of the government (and indeed presumably of a great many voters, taxpayers, patients and also employees of the NHS) that the NHS and other public enterprises not exposed to the competitive discipline of the market place should be required to assess their own performance, and additionally to be audited and assessed independently, to provide a perspective on the level or standard of VFM being attained and to provoke improvement therein. This is all part and parcel of the present government's overall thrust to lower costs or improve performance throughout the public sector, known as the 'FMI', the financial management initiative.

**2.7** The 'Three Es' are 'economy, efficiency and effectiveness'. They embody concepts widely understood and practised in the private sector, which of course is subject to the many pressures of market forces. Many health service professionals instinctively react against such concepts, picturing them as the antithesis of the essentially caring nature of their work. These nevertheless do have an important role in the public sector, where research has repeatedly indicated that, although service standards may well be kept high, high productivity and avoidance of waste are not equally assured.

**2.8** To understand the context of economy, efficiency and effectiveness, three other words first need a brief explanation:

1   Inputs – the resources that are used to obtain or provide something, or to get something done. Examples include staff, equipment, buildings, energy sources and, of course, their common currency, the money needed to acquire them.
2   Outputs – the number of things which are provided or which get done. Examples include patients treated, operations performed, miles travelled, articles laundered and so on.
3   Outcomes – the quality of those outputs, such as the success of treatments, the palatability of meals, the comfort of ambulance journeys. These are the most difficult things to define, measure and cost.

The costs of inputs have always been recorded and monitored. But the exact use or consumption of input resources in producing particular outputs often has not been measured. We need this information, and measures of activity/workload/throughputs, in order to monitor performance and value-for-money in the outputs achieved. Some outputs are simply 'intermediate' or 'facilitating', like X-rays, in the sense that they are but means to the end of better 'final' outputs – and outcomes – in the successful treatment and care of patients.

**2.9** 'Economy' simply means spending or consuming as little as feasible, be it minimizing the use of swabs, electricity, polish, paper clips or whatever. Simple cost figures such as cost per operation in a given specialty, or physical performance figures such as miles per gallon, are examples of measurements of economy. But economy is an unsophisticated concept, as it takes no account of the outputs achieved in using resources. As such it has only limited managerial relevance, although the concept may be useful as part of a general climate of thrift, and as a precept guiding the instruction or supervision provided for junior staff carrying out routine activities.

**2.10** 'Efficiency' is a more complex notion than 'economy', as it takes account of outputs as well as inputs. Efficiency is usually expressed as some direct, linked relationship between outputs and inputs. Thus, to follow through the two example cited in the preceding paragraph, if the cost per operation is related not just to the specialty, but also to the diagnostic status, severity level and treatment output provided, it then becomes a useful measure of efficiency. Similarly, miles per gallon is meaningless unless we relate this to particular outputs supplied by, for example, staff cars, ambulances or works lorries. Thus, passenger miles per gallon (for cars or ambulances), or ton miles per gallon (for lorries and vans) become meaningful measures of 'efficiency'. One can improve efficiency either by increasing output while holding input constant (or reducing it), or by holding output constant while reducing inputs.

But of course the efficiency concept of itself tells us nothing about the need for, or benefit from, any change in output. Nor does it take account of the quality of outcomes, the quality and value of service to patients. Nevertheless it is a useful concept for emphasis in short-term operational management, as there is a reasonable presumption that if the output is essentially unaltered (in quality as well as in quantity) but the resource inputs (and therefore costs are reduced, then this must be a good result to the extent that funds released from this use are put to work to increase or improve some other area of health care delivery.

**2.11** 'Effectiveness' is an even more refined concept. At its purest it relates not just to the volume and cost of outputs, as in efficiency measurement, but also to the quality achieved, i.e. the outcomes. It also implies consideration of the relative benefit obtainable from the use of resources in one activity as compared to another (see the 'opportunity cost' concept explained in the next chapter). NHS outcomes are its effects on the health state and well-being of patients. The problem is that we do not yet know how to measure health care outcomes in objective terms such as will permit making judgements of comparative benefit or effectiveness between, for example, using resources to reduce the waiting list for artificial hip joints instead of for renal dialysis.

The Körner Steering Group has encouraged increased research and development effort to derive useful measures of the quality of outcomes. The result is that 'effectiveness' in practical usage tends to become devalued to mean much the same as efficiency i.e. some measure of performance relative to resource consumption, in the context of individual priorities or policies. When the resource consumption is expressed in monetary terms, the measure becomes a 'cost effectiveness' indicator.

## The 'Three Es' in practice – some international comparisons

**2.12**  It is frequently noted that the UK spends only about six per cent of GNP (i.e. gross national product) on health care, whereas most other non-communist developed countries (notably excepting Japan) spend from seven to over ten percent of GNP on health care. Some commentators may infer from this that the NHS must therefore be more economical and efficient, if not also more effective (or at least cost-effective), than the health services of other nations (excepting Japan again, in this and in all that follows). Since *economy* is simply minimizing expenditure, it follows that the NHS is the most economical health service.

Comparative *efficiency* is more difficult to assess because statistics on inputs and their costs, and on outputs, are often not directly comparable between countries. However, it does seem likely that the lower relative expenditure on health services in the UK can be explained broadly by the combination of the following factors: an effective family doctor service enables a lower rate of hospitalization than is found needful in other countries; remuneration to the UK medical profession largely by salary or capitation reduces the level of often unnecessary medical and (especially) surgical intervention in clinical care alleged to occur more frequently in other countries where payment is more often on an item-of-service basis; administration costs are exceptionally low in the UK, partly because of there being no need to staff marketing or customer-billing services; hospital premises are older and more primitive in the UK, so that capital costs are lower; capital funds are supplied to the NHS at no charge, that is, without requirement to earn a profit, or to pay interest or capital redemption (such as would normally be expected even from UK local and water authorities, and nationalized industries); and of course influencing most of the above characteristics is the decisive factor of the way the NHS is funded centrally, mainly from general taxation, with its scale of resources determined by national political choices rather than by local will or market forces.

**2.13**  Paradoxically, while effectiveness in individual services at the local level is difficult to evaluate in objective terms, and comparisons between different health districts are often bedevilled by claims of distinctively different local needs, or distinctively different local service provisions, at the national level many of these differences 'average out' and allow international comparisons of *effectiveness* by review of relative health status indicators. On the latter criteria the UK comes off quite well in direct comparison with its industrial peer group in Europe (France, Germany and Italy), and with the USA. But the UK compares less well with the health status of, in particular, Scandinavia and the Netherlands, although there is some presumption that the social and educational characteristics of these smaller nations are more supportive to the maintenance of good health (for example, in the minimization of perinatal mortality).

Nevertheless, and in spite of the overall reasonably good performance of the UK in the health status indicators' league table, there are a number of significant 'black spots', some of them well known: the relatively long waiting lists for a wide variety of 'elective' treatments including hip replacements, the lack of adequate renal services, the slow rate of fall in perinatal mortality, often substandard domiciliary provision for the elderly and other long-stay patients, and an overall impression of some shortage of facilities and equipment for delivering the latest medical technology to all who might benefit.

**2.14**  Many ill persons recover, or at least survive for extended periods, if provided with adequate food, warmth, hygiene and caring attention, regardless of the scale or quality of formal medical intervention in their treatment. Bearing this in mind, together with the cost-saving advantages of the UK system of funding and limiting health care expenditure summarized in the preceding paragraph, it is not self-evident that the UK's health services are more efficient than those of other countries, as distinct from being simply more economical, Spartan and 'rationed'. Thus, there are no grounds for complacency through simple comparisons of UK and international levels of expenditure on health services, relative to the health status indicators reported. (See *Health and Wealth* by R.J. Maxwell for a good discussion of international comparisons and the policy issues arising.)

## The task ahead

**2.15**  It must be clear to all readers of this book that in some areas of medical care there is unmet need for acute treatment, and unfulfilled opportunity for higher standards of continuing care in respect of long-stay patients. It would be pleasant to have extra funding, and thus extra staffing and facilities, so as to improve the service without disturbing existing patterns of work and levels of productivity. But this is not likely to occur in presently foreseeable political or economic conditions. And whilst the NHS enjoys general public sympathy and approval, it cannot count upon universal public approval for any major increases in its funding until such time as it can demonstrate to the public that it is both a highly efficient and highly effective organization which, even after achieving high productivity and minimal waste, still cannot cope with the public need and demand for health care.

An objective of this book, and a practical benefit of the various new developments in financial and other management information systems being introduced into the NHS, is to (a) assist health authority members, chairman, officers, managers, clinicians, nurses and other professionals to improve the efficiency (and effectiveness) of their organizations; and (b) provide better measures of performance to monitor that all practicable improvement in efficiency and effectiveness has been achieved, so that if there still remain unmet needs, or low standards of care or caring, then at least there will be objective evidence – and thus a stronger case – that the NHS genuinely needs a higher rate of growth in resources.

**2.16** The funding and budgets of any organization set limits to its overall structure – its shape, size and character. The unit costs of individual activities represent building blocks from which the overall (budgetary) structure is constructed.

Of course, the structure may collapse if the foundations are not sound. In our analogy the foundations consist of the work-units and other measures of activity to which the unit costs relate. For the purpose of this book we assume that the Körner and other initiatives will succeed in improving activity and workload information, thus providing firm and robust foundations.

In the next two chapters we explain the concepts and uses of costs and budgets which must be understood and applied in order to structure an effective financial management information system for the NHS.

## Summary

1 Crude statistics indicate that 'productivity' in the NHS has risen gradually over the past ten years. Presumably this is largely because the demand for health care, and the perceived opportunities to provide care, have risen more rapidly than the funding and resources available (after adjusting for inflation, shorter working hours of some staff, etc.). This can only mean that NHS resources are under tighter pressure than ever before, and so every possible aid must be used to achieve better understanding and control over these resources and their deployment.

2 Better financial and workload information can serve three purposes:
   — meet parliamentary and cash-limits requirements;
   — help managers and clinicians understand how to get the best output of service delivery from their limited resources; and provide detailed evidence of 'good housekeeping' as part of the case when arguing for future increases in resource allocations and budgets.

3 In practical terms for the NHS:
   — economy means avoiding waste (e.g. unused food, spoiled tests);
   — efficiency means controlling for unnecessary tests, empty beds, unused theatre sessions, length of stay, etc., so as to spread budgeted resources across a larger number of patients; and
   — effectiveness means monitoring quality of care so far as measurable, and also moving any underutilized resources to new developments and other areas of maximum benefit to patients.

4 The financial performance of the NHS must be kept in perspective. International comparative health indicators suggest that the health of the British population is overall probably no worse than the average among developed nations, whereas total public and private expenditure on health care in the UK is apparently at least 20 % below the average. The NHS is a low-cost, relatively efficient service.

5 All branches of the public sector have been required by Government to develop detailed information systems for management use and tighter management and audit controls, in order to demonstrate to Government that resources are used increasingly efficiently (and, one hopes, effectively). Institutions which do not quickly develop better information systems, and individual managers and clinicians who do not make good use of them, will increasingly find themselves in weak bargaining positions in the quest for higher funding, bigger budgets and more resources.

# CHAPTER 3
# Costs and costing in the NHS

**3.1**  Few persons committed to the NHS as health authority members, clinical or other professional staff or managers – aside from finance staff – have had the opportunity to study costing and budgetary methods, or the confusion and complications which can arise in using the various concepts and measures of 'cost'. Therefore this chapter and the next will attempt to explain these matters concisely, providing a context for easier understanding of the chapters to follow. This chapter covers cost measures and concepts, while Chapter 4 will cover the characteristics of effective budgetary planning and control.

**3.2**  It has first to be explained that the two terms 'costs' and 'budgets' have distinctively different meanings in accountancy. Basically, costs are measures of loss of monetary value when a resource is acquired or consumed, whereas budgets are 'costed plans' or statements of allowable expenditure over a period of time. And whereas budgets are the responsibility of individual managers and are closely linked with managerial planning, accountability and performance, costs are mainly recorded and monitored at a more detailed, or disaggregated, level – for example, the cost of individual inputs (e.g. a unit of energy cost for steam and heating), the cost of particular activities (e.g. the labour, supplies and other expenses combined to indicate the full cost of a type of diagnostic test), or the cost of outputs (e.g. the costs of inputs and activities combined over a period of time so as to identify average cost per inpatient day or per case).

The main interest in both costs and budgets is in the current figures for use in monitoring and control, and in the fine-tuning of short-term operational decisions. However, past costs and budget outturns are also often of interest for assessment of performance trends, while estimates of future costs are of importance for decision-making, planning and forward budgeting.

Cost data provide the 'building blocks' with which budgets are constructed, as we shall consider further in the next chapter. One can have costing systems without also having budgets, but one cannot have a budget system without also having a costing system to provide the cost or expenditure figures to set against the budgets to monitor progress.

## Measures and concepts of costs and costing

### Actual cost

**3.3**  Actual cost is the amount of money paid (or, if payment is not made at once, the monetary value of the debt incurred) to secure the use of a resource (e.g. payroll) or its possession ready for use later (e.g. equipment, drugs, provisions). Actual costs tend to be higher than they may appear: for example, an employee engaged at £6,000 p.a. is likely to cost about £7,500 p.a. or more to employ after overheads such as employer's National Insurance and superannuation contributions are added in; and the purchase price of a piece of equipment may comprise only a fraction of its total actual cost, once the costs of selecting, ordering, installing, testing and establishing maintenance arrangements are taken into account. These examples show that, far from being a simple matter of fact, actual cost is an amount of expenditure defined by rules about what is to be included and what is not. And those rules must be precisely specified, clearly understood and painstakingly applied if the information system which they support is to yield useful results.

### Total, direct and indirect costs

**3.4**  Total cost, as the term implies, is the sum of all the costs of carrying out an activity or providing a service, or of running a department, ward, clinic or specialty, etc. Total cost comprises 'direct costs' (e.g. for staff employed, drugs and supplies, and equipment, etc.) plus 'indirect costs' of services supplied by other departments (such as the costs of diagnostic tests, paramedical services, catering and so on). For the examples of indirect costs cited, the volume of the services utilized is determined by medical or nursing staff, who thus strongly influence the scale of provision and the long-term costs.

There are other indirect costs over which medical and nursing staff, or service department heads, have little or no influence which affect the volume or cost of provision: these are termed 'overheads' and are discussed further below.

**3.5**  Strictly, costs can be any of 'direct', 'indirect' or 'overhead' in status, depending on how they are measured and controlled. Take cleaning as an example. If ward or departmental managers are free to determine the volume and standard (i.e. costliness) of cleaning, and if this volume of cleaning is measured, costed and chargeable to the ward or department, then cleaning is a direct cost. Or, if the volume of cleaning is measured, costed and charged to the department or ward, but the standards (and therefore largely the volume and costliness, short of influencing these indirectly by, for example, closing beds) are controlled by a domestic services manager, then cleaning is an indirect cost. Or, finally, if cleaning is provided to a common standard throughout a hospital or unit, and it is not measured and costed separately for each ward or department, then cleaning is simply an overhead cost.

Which category any particular cost element falls into is thus determined by a combination of (a) organizational responsibility for the standards and the volume of the service, (b) the level of detail and accuracy of the workload measurement, recording and costing systems in use, and (c) a judgement on whether or not the extra expense of using more sophisticated workload measurement, recording and costing procedures to enable direct charging is likely to save more money than it costs or else usefully improve the efficiency or effectiveness of operations.

*Overhead costs*

**3.6** The overhead costs of an organization are the costs of support services which, while they contribute to the general running of the organization, cannot be directly related to the volume or quality of activity or service provided in individual departments, wards, etc. Overheads include the co-ordinating and managerial activities of senior staff and their departments, including the costs of planning, personnel, payroll and financial management functions. Rates or payments in lieu, and some kinds of insurance payments and subscriptions, are examples of external overheads on behalf of the organization as a whole.

Ancillary services such as heating, laundry, catering and equipment maintenance are overheads which can be charged as indirect costs. Installing separate controls and meters in each department would allow heating to be treated even as a direct cost, although this might have no managerial substance unless departmental management has authority to determine heating levels independent of district or unit norms. Laundry and catering is easily costed on a unit basis (i.e. per item), with the volume of uptake measured to individual departments, so that these can be charged as indirect costs.

We have previously considered how cleaning could be treated in any of the three ways. Maintenance of departmental plant and equipment can easily be measured and costed as indirect services to the departments concerned; however, the general maintenance of grounds, car parks and buildings is a good example of a major cost where the measurement and costing traceable shares of cost responsibility is normally impracticable, or certainly arbitrary.

In the cases of such 'true' overheads either the costs should simply be reported and controlled centrally, or if redistribution to the accounts of departments and wards etc, is required (as we shall consider later in the context of the Griffiths Inquiry recommendations), then some system of approximation must be used. The accountancy term for this is 'apportionment'. Thus general estates expense and rates may be apportioned to departments on the basis of their square-footage of space occupied. Other bases for apportionment can be in proportion to beds in use, workload, total budget, total payroll or otherwise, as may seem most reasonable relative to the form of benefit provided by individual areas of overhead cost.

*Average cost and unit cost*

**3.7** Average cost is the 'mean' average of the individual costs of a whole series of expenditures or uses of resources relating to a particular activity or department. Average costs are typically expressed as *unit costs*, i.e. average costs per unit or item of activity. The most prominent unit costs in the NHS are cost per case and cost per day for acute, inpatient treatment, but of course the 'unit' of standardized measurement can be at a much more immediate, operational level, as, for example, the average cost of a particular class of meal, the average cost of petrol or maintenance per vehicle-mile travelled, or the average cost of a standard dose of a particular drug at the time it leaves the pharmacy for ward use.

Routine reporting of costs related to activity is typically expressed in 'average costs per unit', often simply labelled 'cost', in a way which may often prove more misleading than helpful. The following paragraphs will attempt to substantiate this statement, and to explain what alternative measures of cost should be sought from finance staff to provide more relevant and more useful information for planning and decision-making, as well as for control and subsequent performance measurement and review.

*Fixed costs and variable costs*

**3.8**   Fixed costs are costs which tend to be constant over a period of time, regardless of normal variations upwards or downwards in the level of workload or volume of output. Examples include rates, maintenance contracts, heating and many other overheads, and most staff salaries. Many costs classified as 'fixed' in normal accounting practice are of course subject to variation over longer time-spans. For example, the demolition of a hospital wing may enable rates, heating and often other overheads to be reduced, and reorganization of staff workload on the occasion of the departure of a member of staff may allow the staffing establishment, and thus the fixed-cost element in staffing, to be reduced.

Strictly, many costs in the NHS (as in other organizations) are not rigidly 'fixed' even for periods of time shorter than one year (i.e. the period of time when operational plans, staffing and resource requirements in general have to be reviewed as part of the annual budgetary cycle). Given substantial volume changes downwards, new staff vacancies can be frozen and beds or diagnostic equipment etc. can be taken out of use. Similarly, on rising volume new staff can be appointed and new beds or equipment brought into use (funds and space permitting).

Such situations give rise to what are often called semi-fixed or stepped-cost functions of cost behaviour. This is illustrated in Fig. 3.1, which shows both the stepped fixed-cost function which represents reality, and also the straight horizontal line which represents the normal accounting convention that, at least throughout any one accounting and budget year, the fixed costs will tend to remain constant regardless of short-term changes in the workload or volume of activity (barring exceptional changes outside the normal volume range of activity).

It will be noted in Fig. 3.1 that the fixed costs are a very high proportion of total costs. This occurs because the NHS is a labour-intensive service industry where payroll costs are a high proportion (70–75 %) of total costs, and where most payroll costs are more fixed than variable in character for purposes of short-term operational management and control, within annual budgets.

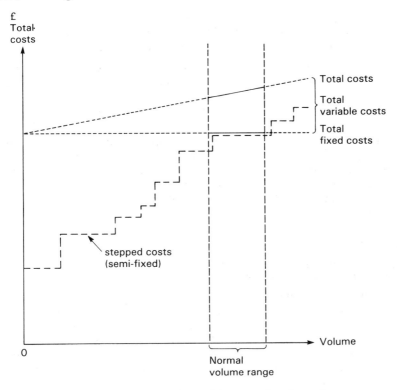

*Fig. 3.1  Total fixed and variable costs related to volume.*

**3.9**  Variable costs are costs which tend to vary in constant proportion to changes in the volume of activity or workload. Examples include provisions, drugs, CSSD packs, etc. There are also semi-variable costs which vary in the direction of change in the volume of activity or workload, but not in a direct or constant proportion. For example one would not expect the laundry requirement in a hospital to fall by precisely one half if it were to happen that the bed-occupancy level fell by fifty per cent in the short term and without any wards being closed.

As in the case of semi-fixed costs explained above, there is a natural tendency in practice for accountants to concentrate on the level of cost at the normal level or volume of operations, and therefore to treat both variable and semi-variable costs together as if all were fully variable. This is also shown in Fig. 3.1, where total variable cost at any given level of volume is represented by the relevant point on the straight line for variable cost.

Whereas with fixed costs it seems reasonable that close scrutiny in most cases need be given only at the time of annual budget reviews (except for the automatic review of the need for posts when vacancies arise during the year in staffing establishments), with variable costs monitoring and control should be exercised by every manager on a continuing, often day-by-day basis. This monitoring and control can be achieved by managers using departmental records of staff time, materials used, etc., in between monthly reports of cost expenditure compared to budget.

**3.10** In summary, every cost that is incurred can be classified either as fixed (or semi-fixed) or as variable (or semi-variable), and every item of health services expenditure can be analysed into one or other of these categories. But these *total* fixed and *total* variable costs are of limited usefulness as they stand. To be of use for control, comparison and planning purposes they must be combined with the unit cost approach described in 3.7 above. Whenever accountants refer to fixed and variable costs in the context of cost analysis they are usually referring to the fixed and variable elements within a unit cost: thus, cost per pathology test (the unit cost) may perhaps be £2, made up of a fixed and semi-fixed total of £1.60 and a variable and semi-variable total of 40p per unit.

*Marginal cost*

**3.11** A marginal cost is the cost of one additional unit of activity: in the example just quoted, one additional test is likely to cost 40p, the variable cost element of the unit cost.

Accountants tend to relate marginal costs very closely to variable costs: if one extra test is 40p, then they say ten extra will be £4 and a hundred extra £40. This is confusing because the concept of marginal cost derives from economics and does *not* accept the assumption that the additional cost of each extra unit of workload will remain constant throughout the workload range which might be worked.

Figure 3.2 attempts to illustrate the difference between the economist's and the accountant's models. The economist's model (which originally was derived for a factory or other commercial environment) assumes that there are inefficiencies in the use of both labour and facilities at low-volume levels, that these are eliminated as volume rises to the optimal level (i.e. the lowest point on the economist's marginal cost (MC) curve), and that a different set of inefficiencies (e.g. overcrowding, equipment overload, worker stress, etc.) arises beyond the optimal volume to cause the cost of each extra unit (i.e. the marginal cost) to rise continually, and at an ever-steeper rate, as the volume exceeds the optimal level. This economist's basic model is set in the context of short-term decision-making, and it therefore takes capital (i.e. the provision of space and equipment etc.) as given or fixed.

The economist's model has useful applications in health service policy and planning, and it is helpful in alerting us that variable cost per unit can differ at changing levels of volume, even if the assumption that any change in volume of even a single unit will alter the level of unit variable cost is unrealistic.

*Incremental cost*

**3.12** Figure 3.2 displays also the basic accounting model for the level of variable (or marginal) cost throughout the volume range. As the accountant's model assumes that the extra (i.e. variable) cost per unit of

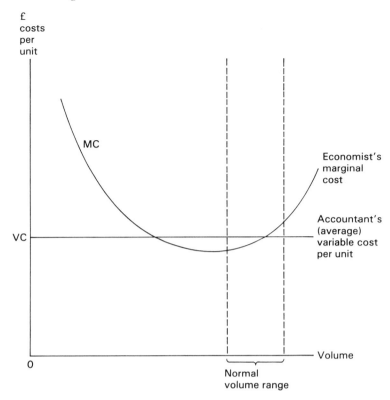

*Fig. 3.2    Comparison of marginal and average variable unit costs.*

extra output is the same regardless of the existing level of output, the result is a horizontal line on Fig. 3.2.

It is unfortunate that both the economist's and the accountant's basic models are unrealistic other than for very small changes in the volume of activity or workload, such as are anyway not likely to require conscious managerial review or decision. This is because in the real world of the NHS most significant managerial (including clinical) decisions on the level of activity and the disposition of resources to support that activity (e.g. as manifested through changes in beds in use, operating theatre time, rate of patient throughput, etc.) will involve some changes that alter the level of fixed costs (i.e. stepped costs) as well as the total of variable costs. For example, an additional member of staff, or the purchase of a major piece of equipment, may be needed. The specification of the extra costs or savings of every significant decision altering the volume of service provision must be individually calculated to take account of all changes in the fixed costs as well as of changes in the marginal/variable costs. This combined analysis of change in fixed plus variable cost is sometimes termed *incremental cost analysis* (not to be confused with 'incremental budgeting' which will be discussed in Chapter 4).

*Relevant cost*

**3.13**  In routine bookkeeping and reporting of expenditure in connection with payments to staff and suppliers, and for monitoring to check that expenditure is within cash limits and budgets, it will be obvious that all costs must be included. This should be distinguished from the use of cost information for planning and decision-making, where only costs which will alter as the result of a decision, or a change of plan, should be included. These are the 'relevant costs'.

For example, if a clinician is considering a change of policy so as to reduce the number of diagnostic tests to be used for particular types of patients, the size of the reduction will probably not be great enough to allow the diagnostic department to cut down on staff or equipment – thus the department's fixed costs will not be altered, and will not be relevant. The 'relevant costs' for the purpose of calculating savings will be for chemicals or other supplies, possibly electric power, and possibly call-out payments to staff if at least part of the reduction in testing can be achieved outside normal working hours.

Of course, if a number of clinicians were to act together, then the scale of reduction in testing activity might enable the next technician vacancy in the diagnostic department to be left unfilled, or the replacement (capital and maintenance) cost of a testing machine to be avoided. In this latter case costs normally thought of as 'fixed' in a long-term situation become 'variable' *and* 'relevant' to the particular decision under consideration.

*Controllable costs*

**3.14**  All costs are controllable by some person or level of management somewhere in the organization. 'Controllable' here means that someone (or occasionally it could be a collective group responsibility) has the authority and therefore also the accountability and responsibility for the existence and continuation – and the precise level – of each element of cost. It is most important to identify the locus of responsibility for all costs, first to assist financial discipline and the administration of cost improvement programmes, and secondly to provide a realistic framework for budgetary planning and control.

Continuing our example of a diagnostic department, it is clinicians who control the volume of testing done, and therefore it is they who are responsible for the relevant costs. In the short term these costs are only the variable costs, but over the longer term and taking clinicians collectively, it is they who determine the total volume of testing activity and who therefore are at least partly responsible for the volume of staffing and equipment expenditure in the particular diagnostic department (i.e. the fixed costs). Nevertheless, once general decisions regarding the scale of staffing and equipment provision for a department have been taken, it will be the department head who exercises control on an ongoing basis, obtaining the correct mix of skills and grades of staff, setting rotas of work to avoid unnecessary overtime, and taking decisions on equipment maintenance and replacement so that a good balance is achieved between cost economy and service capacity and reliability.

Overall this example illustrates how, for diagnostic and also other kinds of service departments, responsibility for costs, and their control, can be divided between the departmental providers of the service output, and the clinicians who determine the volume of workload.

*Standard costs*

**3.15** Paragraph 3.3. above described actual cost and pointed out some of the complexities of calculating it. But there is another problem: whilst it is possible to calculate an actual cost accurately once all the bills have been settled and the salaries paid, it is virtually impossible to state promptly with any certainty the exact cost of, for example, a drug prescribed last week or an X-ray performed yesterday, as prices may have risen, pay awards may be applied restrospectively, overtime worked, and so on. Yet if costs are to be controlled, the prompt reporting of costs incurred is vital.

To overcome this problem – or, more precisely, to circumvent it – 'standard costs' (a term and technique adapted from industrial accounting) are sometimes employed. Standard costs are target levels of cost per unit of activity which have been calculated or otherwise agreed as representing a fair level of performance and efficiency. Thus, for instance, one might determine a schedule of standard costs for all the main categories of diagnostic tests, including the costs of labour, supplies and any indirect costs controllable by departmental management. Each year the cost standards would need review and updating, to take account of inflation or other price and salary changes, and of any changes in technology or methods of working.

Standards are set separately for the variable costs and the fixed costs. The standard fixed costs, plus any part of the overall variable costs unrelated to the level of clinical demand for tests, would be deemed the controllable responsibility of the diagnostic department head, while the standard cost of resources consumed in actual testing, as well as the extra costs of call-out activity, would be identified as the controllable responsibility of clinicians. Indeed these calculations can be the basis for determining budgets and operating budgetary control in a system of clinical management budgets.

**3.16** It is possible to supply quickly the total standard costs (i.e. actual volumes multiplied by unit standard costs) incurred in each diagnostic (or other service) department, with the relevant clinician-controlled costs segregated and indeed reported to each clinician – provided that the workload control system is operated effectively so as to capture accurately the name of each clinician responsible for each test carried out. Aside from the advantage of the much prompter supply of control information when using standard costs, there is the further advantage of the stability and comparability of the figures through the year, because market price and pay changes etc. are of course excluded from the standard cost until the next review and revision.

When finance staff eventually obtain and check all the information needed to determine the total actual costs of a department or activity for a period of time, the expected result would normally be that the total standard costs recorded for the actual volume of work completed will not be the same as the total costs. The difference between the two figures is termed the 'total variance'. For example:

| | |
|---|---:|
| Total actual costs for May in Dept. P | £54,592 |
| Total standard costs for May in Dept. P | £50,361 |
| Total variance for May in Dept. P | £ 4,231 |

**3.17** In the above illustration the total variance is 'unfavourable', given that actual costs have exceeded the total standard costs which represent the target level of cost (or, notionally, the achieved value of completed work) for the actual volume of output supplied. Entire textbooks are written to explain the full complexities of standard costing and variance analysis for accountants, and it is not practicable to go into detail here. Suffice it to state that with appropriate records and analyses, it is feasible to subdivide the illustrated unfavourable total variance into component sub-variances to explain how far the apparent excess of actual cost was caused by price or payroll changes, by excessive call-outs or overtime, by waste of supplies, or by under-recovery in the standard fixed costs because actual volume had fallen below the target volume of tests used as the basis for setting the standard fixed costs per unit of activity.

This latter aspect is measured by the 'volume variance' which indicates the level of fixed or standing costs which in a sense have been wasted through the shortfall in actual volume, or the figures can be interpreted as indicating the approximate level of cost savings which might be achieved if the volume of activity were permanently reduced, assuming the fixed costs could be scaled down more or less pro rata, as a once-for-all move downwards on the stepped-cost function (as previously explained and illustrated in Fig. 3.1).

**3.18** Standard costing, so far little used in the NHS, offers a potentially powerful tool for better cost control and accountability, as well as providing a basis for constructing budgets. Once any initial systems set-up work were done, the ongoing operation of a standard costing system should be no more expensive than that of a *good, prompt* actual-cost reporting system.

## Expenditure costs v consumption costs

**3.19** Government control over health services' financial expenditure is exercised mainly through cash-limited allocations separately for revenue funds and capital funds. This might seem an inflexible system to cope with variations in health care service needs which may come to attention long after the total funding allocations to regions have been set by government and then reallocated to districts by regions. Nevertheless, in practice there is considerable flexibility at the margin, given permutations of the use of transfers (i.e. 'virement') between revenue and capital allocation, of allowable carryforward of small balances of underspent funds between one year and the next, of end-of-year adjustments to balances of cash, debtors and creditors, and of the role of regions in providing bridging finance, especially to balance out differential timing in the needs for capital and development funds between their districts.

**3.20** Yet while the total expenditure and the rate of timing of expenditure of funds is controlled, and is monitored regionally and centrally, on what is essentially a cash-flow basis, it is true also that the principal basis of NHS financial accountability to government for the detailed use of resources is not on a cash-flow basis, but rather on an 'income and expenditure accounting' basis. The latter includes the use of 'accrual accounting' so that, for example, expenditure liabilities for supplies or equipment received can be included in the accounts at the date of delivery or of other recognition of contractual obligation to pay, rather than the liabilities being ignored (other than on a commitments basis) until the eventual date of cash payment, as would be the case in pure cash-flow accounting as widely used in most activities directly controlled by central government. In other words, the NHS is enabled to use a system of accounting and cost recording which is similar to commercial and local government practice, except that no costs are included for the consumption of capital through depreciation, or for interest costs for the use of capital. These are gaps in contemporary NHS financial practice the implications of which will be discussed in greater detail in Chapter 8.

**3.21** There are local variations between districts both in accounting practice and in purchasing and stores/supply organization and procedures. In some cases the expenditure costs of supplies etc. may be charged direct to the costs (and budgets) of functional departments at the time of initial acquisition, but in other cases this charging may not occur until the supplies etc. are withdrawn from stores and made available for use or consumption in the work of wards, theatres, support services and hotel activities. In both cases the charging to accounts may precede actual physical *consumption* of the resources.

In contrast, staff time and some services such as telephones and electric power may be consumed before the exact cost is known and recorded. Staff time of course represents nearly 75% of total cost in the hospital and community health services. In short, the recording of the cost of consumption of resources is seldom matched in time, side by side with the actual units of activity or workload for which costs are incurred.

**3.22** Returning to the illustration of a diagnostic department, staff costs will be recorded through the payroll system, and supplies and other expenses will be recorded as costs at a variety of dates only coincidentally matching with the date when any particular batch of tests is carried out. Thus, under the present system, neither actual nor standard costs are normally available to record side by side with activity (workload) information to enable the costed workload imposed by each specialty, firm or clinician, to be traced to the source of clinical causation of that workload.

In other words, and barring some districts where improved systems have already been introduced in connection with trials of specialty costing or budgeting or patient costing, NHS costing normally focuses on the cost accountability of the person responsible for the initial expenditure on acquiring resources, rather than on the person or team responsible for the ultimate consumption of resources. Most of the important resource-consumption decisions are taken, or at least are strongly influenced, by doctors, yet up until now they have largely been outside the NHS framework of cost allocation and accountability. Nor do the revenue costs which are recorded include any charges for the use and wearing out of major capital assets, or for interest on the cost or value of those capital assets.

## Costs in performance comparisons and trends

3.23   The brief coverage in this chapter of some characteristics of cost information in the NHS, which is expenditure orientated as distinct from activity/output orientated, illustrates why NHS costs are often in a form not the most useful for judgements on managerial efficiency let alone effectiveness. A similar point is made more generally by the many critics of some of the performance indicators used in performance reviews or published in the regional and national summaries.

Even in the case of what ought to be the most consistently reliable indicators – costs reported routinely for the annual Health Services Costing Returns (which are supposed to be collected on a standardized basis) – there are claims of non-comparability on at least two grounds. First, local differences in organization structure and in bookkeeping systems may mean that some costs are not classified and allocated identically in all districts. Secondly, there is the perennial problem that like is not being compared with like, in that the actual services costed are not identical. That is, for example, the specialty and case mix in acute hospitals is often distinctively different between one hospital and another, and between any one hospital and the average.

3.24   Regardless of the foregoing, it seems clear that internal management at the local level can often learn much from inquiries prompted by the use and review of performance indicators. John Yates and Christopher Day, amongst others, have explained and illustrated how performance indicators, and statistical information more generally, may be made more relevant, understandable and useful. Performance indicators, a term which strictly includes such costing information as cost per unit of activity and also costing and budgetary variances, serve to help managers and health authority members to identify useful questions to ask, even if they seldom directly provide full answers and sometimes even prove to be misleading.

3.25   In this chapter the focus has been on concepts and measures of cost and on problems of cost measurement in the NHS. Later chapters will report on developments in improved cost information which should assist managers and members to achieve better understanding, control and improvement of NHS resources utilization. Costing aside, the other principal type of financial control information system is budgeting, although in practice the two systems are interdependent.

However, whilst this book is primarily concerned to discuss the development and better use of financial information, it should be borne in mind throughout that the postulated improvements in the use of resources can only be attained if activity and manpower information improves in relevance, accuracy and timely availability, keeping in step with better financial information so that cost and budgetary performance can be related at all times to the human and other resources employed in the NHS, and to the activity workload and output achieved thereby.

## Costs and opportunity costs

**3.26** This chapter has briefly explained and illustrated the principal terms (or concepts) and measures used by accountants to classify and report operating costs for planning, decision-making, control and accountability. All this is the work of management accountants, as distinct from the work of financial accountants who are principally concerned to ensure that the cash disbursements of the health authority are for proper purposes, are properly authorized, and are properly recorded and reported in conformity with all regulations, with cash limits on total expenditure, and with statutory requirements for periodic reporting to the DHSS.

But economists also contribute to the concepts or forms of analysis useful in financial management within the NHS. There are three main examples of this. One is the 'marginal cost' approach explained earlier in this chapter. A second is the 'option appraisal' approach to capital and other development projects, linked with 'cost-benefit' and 'cost-effectiveness' analysis, which will be considered in Chapter 8. The third example is the 'opportunity cost' approach, presented in the concluding paragraphs of this chapter because of its conceptual importance.

**3.27** Opportunity cost (briefly mentioned in the preceding chapter) is the value of the benefit forgone because of using money or other resources in a particular investment or activity, rather than in the most beneficial alternative investment or activity. To illustrate this at the personal level, the opportunity cost of trading in an old car to acquire a new one may be that no money is available for a good summer holiday: here one's judgement on how to proceed does not depend just on the respective out-of-pocket costs of the two courses of action, but rather it must take account also of the relative benefits and satisfaction provided by the alternative uses of resources.

Moving to an NHS illustration, take the case of an inner-city hospital on a congested site. An old, decrepit wing is being demolished, but some capital is available for new construction. If the wing is rebuilt as wards, the opportunity will have been lost to use the space for either a vehicle garage or a nurses' home, both of these being developments desired by the health authority. The most attractive of the latter two options, after considering both costs and benefits, defines the net opportunity cost of any decision to rebuild the demolished wing as treatment wards.

**3.28** The example cited above has long-term implications, but often a decision to use revenue funds in a particular way may only involve a short-term opportunity cost commitment in that if the revenue expenditure is non-recurring (i.e. a one-off expenditure, within a single year), or if additional growth or development money will become available in the following year(s), then the question of the best (opportunity) use of funds and real resources can be reviewed at a later stage.

Opportunity cost is not a specific system of cost recording or routine reporting: rather it is an approach to the analysis of costs in decision-making which, in the typical situation that funds and other resources are strictly limited, forces accountants and decision-makers to analyse costs on the basis of recognizing that the use of resources in one activity forecloses their use in other activities. Practically speaking, this signifies that in so far as feasible all alternative, competing uses of scare resources should be considered and evaluated simultaneously, so that their respective costs and benefits may be compared directly and the alternative with the highest net benefit may be selected. 'Net benefit' will normally be some amalgam of the quality and quantity of care to be provided from scarce financial resources. Good budgeting systems can help develop awareness of alternative uses of resources, and their opportunity costs.

## Summary

1 Costs are measures – expressed in money – of resources used or consumed. However, before you can have accurate (and useful) costs information, it is first necessary to have accurate recording and reporting of activity and workload data: exactly what items of resource were used, when, and on whose instruction or accountability.
2 Cost information allows us to examine the detail of the use of resources, and to study trends or be alert for sudden changes in the level or mix of resources used.
3 Cost information provides 'building blocks' for annual planning studies, and for estimating and drafting future budgets for individual budget holders and units of management.
4 Costing systems provide useful information even where no matching budget system is in use. However, it is not possible to have meaningful budgets without a pre-existing costing system, since it is accurate costs which are required both to draft budgets before the start of the budget year, and to monitor progress against budget at least monthly through the budget year.
5 There are many different concepts and terms for defining and classifying cost data. Some are used mainly for control, others for planning and decision-making. These are discussed in the chapter, and most of them are included additionally in the Glossary.
6 In cash-financed public services like the NHS people have become accustomed to equating 'cost' with 'cash expenditure'. This view is not helpful for management control. For example, purchasing drugs is certainly an 'expenditure', but the true 'cost' does not arise until particular drugs are actually consumed by particular patients, on the orders of a particular doctor. Only then do we know where the true cost 'accountability' resides, and to which budget the final cost charge should be made.
7 'Opportunity cost' is a fundamental concept. This recognizes that the most important 'cost' of using resources on one activity is that the opportunity to use those resources on some other activity (which might have higher value or benefit) is foreclosed.
8 NHS costs are largely 'fixed' within annual budgets, typically up to 80% or more. Thus the scope for quick response in making short-run budget adjustments is often limited to changes in the use of consumables, deferring maintenance, or freezing staff vacancies.

# CHAPTER 4
# Budgeting in the NHS

**4.1** Budgets and budgeting must be distinguished from funding allocations. The latter are authorization to spend public money on approved purposes, normally expressed in totals of cash-limited revenue or capital expenditure. They do not normally include a detailed breakdown among the separate activities managed by the organization receiving the allocation, although portions of funding allocations can be 'earmarked' or protected for specific uses, such as the 'joint finance' allocations to districts for joint developments with local authorities.

Funding allocations are often based upon a mechanistic formula in an attempt to introduce objectivity and equity into the allocation process, as in the case of the RAWP targets (i.e. the target allocations based on the formula devised by the Resource Allocation Working Party, which are used to determine relative rates of growth or contraction in the actual funding allocations to individual regional health authorities). An allocation process is usually a 'top down' exercise, in which the higher tier disposes and the lower tier accepts with little or no consultation or opportunity to influence directly the allocation decision.

## Basic features of budgeting

**4.2** Budgeting, properly conducted, is a very different process from a funding allocation. Budgeting starts with a district's given or forecast funding allocation and seeks to divide the total resources available in a detailed breakdown between the competing activities or services which the organization manages. *Good* budgeting is usually a 'top and bottom' exercise, in which the organizational parts (units, departments, specialties or whatever) have the opportunity to propose, innovate and bargain with the district, even if the district at the end of the exercise must remain responsible for often difficult decisions in the division of limited resources between competing uses.

A practical definition of budgets is that they are the operational plans of an organization expressed in monetary terms. The operational plans or programme for the year ahead would make little sense if not fully inter-linked with detailed budgets in a manner which facilitated the achievement of operational planning goals. Indeed monetary budgets are the only way in which one can aggregate all the activities of a health authority – numbers of bed days, prescriptions supplied, X-ray tests, and square metres cleaned cannot be added together – in order to obtain a perspective of the entire woods as distinct from individual trees.

## Incremental budgeting

**4.3** During the years of continual growth in NHS expenditure in 'real terms' (i.e. after allowing for inflation) the most common form of budget preparation in the NHS was 'incremental budgeting'. That is, typically, each NHS budget from the previous year was adjusted upwards for expected inflation in the next year to provide a baseline, or starting point for the next year's budget. The total of these inflation adjusted budgets was then deducted from the the total expected funding allocation to determine the excess, i.e. the growth money or the 'increment', available for distribution. Claims from budget holders for a share in the increment were then invited, and were assessed, compared and shortlisted. Existing activities and cost levels went largerly unchallenged, and attention was focused almost entirely on achieving the best division, or the division most acceptable to consensus, of the incremental funds. Hence the term 'incremental budgeting'.

The antithesis of incremental budgeting is 'zero-base budgeting', where the continuation of *all* existing activities is challenged, and this alternative approach will be discussed later in this chapter. In between these two extremes is an approach to budgeting which insists that budget baselines should be determined only after conscious judgements on expected future workload and on the efficiency of resource-use, and needful costs, to achieve that workload.

## Workload and cost-based budgeting

**4.4** The taking of last year's price-adjusted budgets as a baseline for the coming year is in effect an abrogation of responsible budgeting. Budgets are costed plans. Operational plans should be based on explicit objectives, supported by estimates of the workload required to achieve realizable objectives. The estimated workload should then be assessed for resource requirements in manpower, space, equipment and consumables, and the results should be costed. Resource-costed workloads are thus the method for constructing rational budgets.

Of course, it may often occur, even under this approach, that when all proposed budgets are added together they exceed available financial resources, or at least leave too little margin for new developments given high priority by the authority. In such cases budget holders will have to be asked to think again about their objectives and proposed workload, and also about the possibilities for more cost-efficient use of their resources.

In short, the process of agreeing final budgets is an iterative process of negotiation between budget holders and top management until something near an optimum distribution of budget resources is achieved.

*Fixed budgets*

**4.5** The simplest form of budgets are termed 'fixed budgets'. They authorize a single, fixed total of expenditure for a specified period of time, and within the fixed total budget there may be numerous sub-budgets for individual resources, activities or expenses. Each sub-budget can itself be treated as a fixed budget not to be exceeded, or some switching of funds between sub-budgets may be allowed so long as the fixed total budget is held to.

This is a somewhat complicated matter considered in the wider context of budgetary control incentives and sanctions later in this chapter. But, overall, fixed budgets are an appropriate form of budget to use when for policy reasons it is considered essential to restrain expenditure within predictable limits. Even in the industrial sector fixed budgets are often used, especially for limiting head office expense, expenditure on R&D (research and development), and sometimes advertising and promotion costs as well. However, there is the classic tale of the industrial firm whose sales reps sat in the office the last few days of most months, because they had used up their fixed-budget allowance for petrol and other travelling expenses for that month!

In industry and commerce many budgets must be flexible to respond to changing levels of sales and demand – a fixed budget for production costs would be a nonsense if there were both unfilled orders and underused capacity. But of course the industrial model is not wholly transferable to the NHS, where the overall fixed budget (i.e. allocation) of the district inhibits major short-term increases in the volume of throughput, with changes in the length of the waiting list serving as the supply/demand regulator.

*Flexible budgets*

**4.6** Proper budgets are constructed by the use of building blocks composed of relevant and accurate cost data. Approached in this way, draft budgets are simply the aggregation of the allowable cost per unit of activity, multiplied by the expected or authorized workload expressed in units of activity. Past 'actual costs' with uplift for inflation can be used to build targets. But whenever feasible, it is on the whole usually more effective to install standard costing (as discussed in the preceding chapter) for use in building (and controlling) budgets. Where a standard costing system correctly differentiates between fixed and variable costs, as it should do, then this subdivision can be built into the budgets as well. It will greatly improve the sensitivity of budgetary performance monitoring and control by managers, month by month through the year. Additionally it will allow the use of 'flexible budgets'. This is a form of budgeting in which the fixed costs are firmly budgeted as a flat amount for a given period of time, but the variable costs are expressed as an allowable (standard) unit cost for each unit of activity, linked with a statement of the target or expected number of units of activity. The fixed-cost budget remains fixed over the year, but the variable-cost budget goes up and down in direct proportion to the volume of activity experienced.

**4.7** The method of flexible budgeting is widely used in industry, where any increase in volume of activity in departments normally reflects a rise in sales and therefore an inflow of revenue to a degree greater than the rise in the variable costs of production to meet demand. It is of course much more difficult to use flexible budgeting in the NHS, where total revenue is normally fixed for the year by cash limits. So flexible budgeting will only work in the NHS for very small budgets, or if the treasurer maintains substantial reserves to cover this contingency (but see later discussion of the risks of this), or if by good luck and very active management from the centre it proves possible to hold back expenditure in lower priority areas in order to finance rising variable cost spending in higher priority activities able to expand their supply. However, even if flexible budgeting is seldom used in the NHS as the formal, principal method of budget management, there are certainly many cases where treasurers attempt to ease managers' problems from rises in total variable costs caused by unpremeditated increases in the activity level, and the term 'flexing the budget' is often applied to this process of budget adjustment, or to virement (see below) between budgets.

## Features of effective budgeting and budgetary control

**4.8**  There are a number of features widely regarded as characteristic of effective budgetary systems, and these are summarized below:

a  Revenue budgeting should be closely integrated with the operational planning process, and capital budgeting should be equally closely linked with the capital and strategic planning processes. Although budgeting and the managerial operation of budgets may appear to be mainly about control, it should be remembered that the managerial definition of control is that it is the process of monitoring progress to verify if it conforms to plan and, if it does not, then to initiate corrective action and ensure feedback into improved planning.

b  Relevant, accurate and timely costing information, preferably in the form of standard costs whenever practicable, is essential, as is also equivalently good activity and manpower information. Standard costs can be reported promptly for monitoring actual volumes of activity, while subsequent analysis of the difference between standard costs and actual costs (termed the 'variance') can identify expenditure problems and assist in identifying the causes.

c  The quality of budgeting will be higher if all relevant managers are involved in the review of alternatives and targets early in the budget planning phase, before budget drafts become too firm and difficult to alter. This applies not just to senior budget holders, but also to more junior management who may be expected to implement delegated budgets for their bosses, as budget 'managers'. Not only is genuine participation in the planning phase of budgeting important to commitment, but also some organizations have found it helpful to commitment, at the end of the budget planning phase, to arrange a 'formal' meeting for each senior manager, together with a budget officer, to meet individually with each of his or her junior managers. These meetings clarify any final problems and obtain commitment from the junior manager that s/he agrees and accepts the budget and will make every effort to conform to it and to the activity, workload and efficiency targets which have been accepted as a reasonable basis for the level of financial budget allowed.

d   The budgetary process should provide managers with encouragement to seek savings in lower priority activities to 'trade off' for extra spending on higher priority or higher benefit activities. This should be possible both during the budget planning phase, and also after the budget year has started. This issue of providing incentives to managers to achieve savings and effective resource transfers is discussed in detail later in this and following chapters: different complications arise depending on whether the budget concerned is functional, unit or clinical. Just as managers should have a channel through which they can negotiate in advance over planned savings, so also should this allow for the possibility of budget holders applying during the year for some increase in current budget on the basis of an argued case of unforeseen need. Of course, in a cash-limited service the opportunities to raise budgets in mid-year will be quite limited unless treasurers maintain large reserves which almost 'invite' late bids for funds.

e   Budgetary control requires frequent monitoring of managers' conformity to budget, plus follow-up of all significant variances from plan or target. Budget holders should receive monthly reports of their performance to budget, setting out variances and preferably giving some indication of the likely cause of any significant variance. In the past there have often been excessive delays in the supply of budget holders' progress reports, but increasing computerization and experience should facilitate more prompt reporting. Monthly reports should be supplied to budget holders before the middle of the following month, for strong motivational encouragement towards quick corrective action. Perhaps needless to stress, the budget reports must be accurate, if interest, credibility and discipline are to be sustained. And the sooner that equally accurate activity statistics (i.e. one form of performance indicators) can be reported side by side with the budgets, and at the same time as the budget spending figures, the better it will be for assisting realization that management control in the NHS is not just about limiting spending, but also, more importantly, about delivering a high volume and quality activity/output from the limited financial and other resources currently available. Summaries of these progress reports should be reported regularly to the health authority members, who with growing experience may be able to contribute usefully to the sense of importance , as well as the content, of effective budgetary planning and control.

f   Effective budgetary planning and control requires more than just efficient data collecting and costing systems – although these are essential prerequisites. It requires an open, collaborative exchange of information and insights between budget holders, budget managers (i.e. those managing parts of budgets on delegated authority from budget holders) and members of the finance staff. In particular, those senior members of finance departments who are assigned liaison roles with budget holders (often working under the title of unit financial adviser) must have the time and interest to establish personal contact with all budget holders, both to consult and advise on technical aspects of budgetary planning and control, and also to explore alternative patterns of resource utilization and to search for savings or improvements in output or quality etc. (i.e. the opportunity cost approach to decision-making). This is difficult, because management cost and manpower controls effectively restrict the size of treasurers' departments and, critically, the number of posts graded to attract and hold fully qualified professional staff. Partly to overcome this problem of insufficient senior staff time for face-to-face contact with budget holders, some treasurers are developing written narrative reports to accompany the routine monthly budget progress reports. The latter are numerical, increasingly they are in the form of computer printouts (for speed and accuracy), and some managers find them difficult to interpret. Narrative reports help to overcome this. Also, computer systems can be used to supply budget holders with graphical reports illustrating both current levels and cumulative trends in expenditure compared to budget allocation, and indeed within a few years it may be possible for budget holders to check their budget position at any time by on-line interrogation of cumulative budget records held on computer complete with colour graphics.

## New dimensions in NHS budgeting

**4.9** At this point an organizational chart of a 'typical' district structured to reflect hierarchical budgetary control relationships could be considered, but the variety of organizational arrangements since the 1982 reorganization makes any single budgetary chart more misleading than typical. So instead a more generalized model will be considered in Fig. 4.1 to illustrate how budgetary responsibility, and the related need to allocate, reallocate and apportion expenditure costs in new ways, has increased the complexity of costing and budgeting in the NHS. Eventually, when all major elements in the NHS financial, activity, manpower and related information systems are fully developed, tested, proven accurate, and able to be brought together in a single, compatible computer network at district level, then and only then will it be feasible to cope quickly and fully with the three-dimensional cost and budgetary complexity illustrated in Fig. 4.1. (NB: Readers will note that the figure is a simplified model, with only a fraction of the total subjective cost categories, functional areas, and typical number of specialties being shown to minimize confusion. There can be up to seventy or more functional areas, fifteen or more specialties and fifty or more individual clinicians, in reasonably typical Districts.)

**4.10** In Fig. 4.1, line AB is subdivided to represent approximately the relative magnitudes of some of the main 'subjective costs' (i.e. costs classified by what the money was spent on). Line BC adds information showing specimen major functions in a district, and the plane defined by lines AB

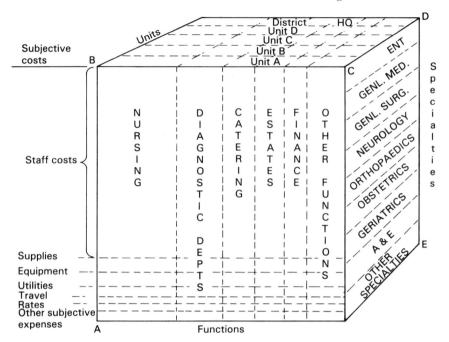

Fig. 4.1   *Budgets subdivided by subjective costs, functional management, management units and specialties (or clinicians).*

and BC displays in matrix format how the subjective costs have to be divided among the functional areas of management to derive the overall division of management responsibility for budgetary control. This was the framework for NHS budgeting between 1974 and 1982.

Line CD is then added to the illustration, this being divided into the number of management units in the district, plus the district headquarters and centrally managed services, as required to provide unit budgets under the 1982 reorganization. The second plane defined by lines BC and CD displays again in matrix format how the subjective costs already divided among the functions have to be re-divided to establish the sub-sets of functional costs budgeted to the responsibility of unit level management.

Finally, line DE introduces a breakdown between a selection of specialties of different sizes, The plane defined by lines CD and DE illustrates how the costs and/or budgets of each unit might be redistributed among the specialties. The illustration shows all the indirect costs and overheads of the district reallocated to the specialties (or the reallocation could be to individual clinicians), even including the cost of estates and of all headquarters activities and services. This would be the literal result of implementing Griffiths Inquiry advice on clinical management budgets. In contrast, the Körner system of costing the work of clinical specialties would stop short of reallocating all the overheads.

**4.11**   Some problems of cost and budgetary control in the established functional budgeting system (plane ABC) and the new unit management budgets (plane BCD) will be considered in the next chapter. Körner Specialty Costing (plane CDE) and related matters will be discussed in Chapter 6, whilst the Griffiths recommendations and CASPE trials (also plane CDE) will be reviewed in Chapter 7. Towards the end of the book, in Chapter 9, a further level of the detailed measurement and allocation of costing, and possibly of budgeting, will be introduced: this relates to costing for patient groups or diagnosis related groups (DRGs), i.e. subdivisions of specialties, and the possibilities for budgeting for a cost-weighted patient case mix or workload.

## Incentives, sanctions and flexibility in NHS budgeting

**4.12**   There is a tradition in the public services, to a much greater extent than in private business, that once budgetary allocations have been agreed (at or before the beginning of the budget year) there should be no changes in expenditure patterns during the year unless approved by higher authority. In other words the degree of devolution or decentralization of authority to managers to switch expenditure from one heading (or sub-budget) to another has been limited, in NHS as in other public services.

Possibly this may have resulted because it was felt that such limitation would make it less likely that the outturn (i.e. final results) of expenditure would attract criticism from auditors or from the reviews of ministers or Parliament. Possibly it may have resulted because treasurers preferred an arrangement whereby any under spendings on particular sub-budgets were not spent by the budget holder, but instead were clawed back to the authority as a whole so as to be available to balance out overspendings which might arise, often unavoidably, in other budgets. Certainly it must have contributed to the fact that most health authorities have underspent their total allocations slightly in most years.

But whatever the cause of the tradition, it seems only sensible, in today's climate of treating NHS budget-holding managers as responsible and accountable decision-makers, that more flexibility in varying expenditure patterns to meet changing needs and opportunities should be allowed and indeed encouraged. To explore this, we must consider NHS practices of 'virement' and 'carry-forward', the question of incentives for budget holders more generally, and also the related questions of sanctions for poor budgetary performance and of whether or not treasurers should hold reserves centrally.

*Virement*

**4.13**   'Virement' is an authorized transfer of funding or allowable expenditure between one allocation, or budget, and another. Thus at authority level the main use of the term relates to transfers between revenue and capital allocations: up to 1% of revenue may be vired to capital, or up to 10% of capital may be vired to revenue. (NB: The greater flexibility for capital arises because it is a much smaller fund, but, more importantly, because weather and other factors outside the control of a health authority can greatly alter the predicted timing of cash expenditure on capital projects.) As will be seen in Chapter 8, there is serious concern that funding health authorities separately for revenue and capital, with only the limited virement flexibility outlined above, may result in a less efficient and effective use of overall resources than if the two allocations were combined, with authorities left to make their own managerial decisions as to the best opportunity-cost use of funds as between revenue and capital expenditures.

**4.14** Within a health authority, at the level of budget holders, virement refers to the process of arranging approved transfers of authorized expenditure from one main budget to another or, sometimes, between one budget heading or sub-budget and another. Many health authorities have sections in their Standing Financial Instructions, or in other formal regulations, which detail precisely how budgetary virement shall operate.

The coverage of virement can extend to several pages, and it is not possible here to discuss every point of detail. However, at the least we must attempt to clarify the main principles involved in virement. Remember here that virement is the switching of funds from one use to another *after* the start of the budget year: changes in spending patterns planned in advance are simply part of the normal operational and budgetary planning cycle.

To make it easier to follow this topic we reproduce in Fig. 4.2 a decision tree diagram which was used by one health authority in its own internal instructions on virement to provide a framework for the following discussion. (Numbers have been entered in the left-hand side of Fig. 4.2 to provide a key, matching the numbered paragraphs below.)

1    The virement issue naturally focuses on situations where the budget is already underspent, or at least where it is predicted to end up underspent. This covers both the case where the budget holder realizes a saving is possible and then casts about for a worthy alternative use, and also the case where some other budget is under pressure to overspend, with its priority so high that the budget holder must search all his other budgets for a lower-priority or more postponable resource use which can be cut back to fund the virement transfer between budgets.

2    It has been a cardinal precept among nearly all treasurers that fortuitous (i.e. unplanned) savings should return to the authority, and should not be allowable as a source of virement to other budgets. Unplanned savings may arise because of delays in filling staff vacancies, price cuts in consumables, or perhaps a fall in the volume of service provided owing to less illness or fewer accidents than expected. Managers often feel that they should be allowed to retain fortuitous savings, and we shall need to return to this issue later when considering unit budgets and clinical budgets, as it may be that modified rules are needed to deal with newer organizational relationships and accountability.

3    A 'planned saving' can be proven to be 'planned' only if the intention to make the saving is declared in advance. Therefore to avoid possible abuse, reduce uncertainty, and encourage conscious forward planning and the updating of budget expectations, most authorities insist that savings plans and proposals for virement are disclosed and discussed in advance, typically through the unit financial adviser.

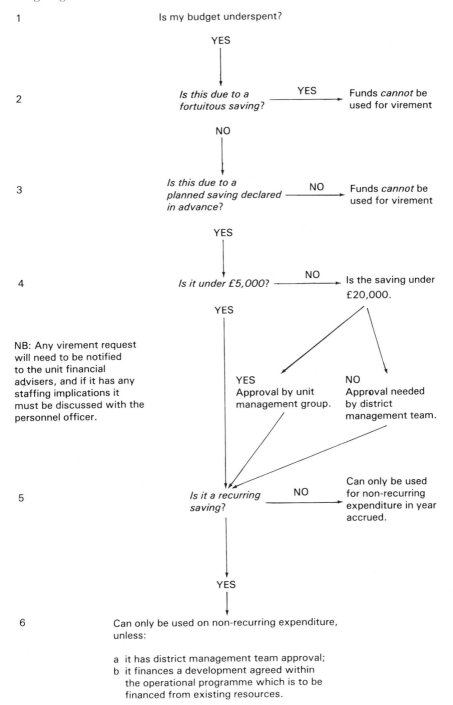

1    Is my budget underspent?

YES

2    *Is this due to a*     ——— YES ———▶    Funds *cannot* be
     *fortuitous saving?*                  used for virement

NO

3    *Is this due to a*     ——— NO ———▶    Funds *cannot* be
     *planned saving declared*             used for virement
     *in advance?*

YES

4    *Is it under £5,000?* ——— NO ———▶    Is the saving under
                                           £20,000.

YES

NB: Any virement request
will need to be notified
to the unit financial                  YES                NO
advisers, and if it has any            Approval by unit    Approval needed
staffing implications it               management group.   by district
must be discussed with the                                 management team.
personnel officer.

5    *Is it a recurring* ——— NO ———▶    Can only be used
     *saving?*                           for non-recurring
                                         expenditure in year
                                         accrued.

YES

6    Can only be used on non-recurring expenditure,
     unless:

     a  it has district management team approval;
     b  it finances a development agreed within
        the operational programme which is to be
        financed from existing resources.

*Fig. 4.2  Virement decision tree.*

4    This illustrates how a small/virement may be immediately allowable
     after forward notice is given and discussed with the adviser, whereas
     larger virements may require approval of the unit management group
     or the district management team. Although this approach is widely
     followed, in the author's experience there is considerable variation
     among authorities in the amounts of money chosen for the various cut-
     off points, and also some authorities require very large virements to be
     approved by the DHA itself. Some authorities specify percentage-of-
     budget figures as additional or alternative criteria for cut-off between
     the different categories of approval required.
5    If a saving is non-recurring (i.e. if it arises from something like delaying
     maintenance or purchase of equipment, or planned delay in filling a
     staff vacancy, so that the saving is only temporary) then naturally the
     related budget transfer can only be into alternative non-recurring
     expenditure within the year in question. Otherwise the authority would
     suffer a net increase in expenditure over a period of years.
6    Even when a saving is recurring (e.g. when an established post is
     abolished, or a permanent switch to lower cost consumables or
     processing is made), most treasurers are prepared to concede virement
     only within the current year (i.e. a non-recurring expenditure),
     although if substantial sums are involved and the savings are to be vired
     into a planned development of high priority to the authority, then it
     may sometimes be possible to negotiate transfer of at least part of the
     savings on a recurring expenditure basis. And sometimes it may not be
     feasible to redeploy savings into the desired alternative cash
     expenditure within the current budget year. In such cases it may be
     possible to negotiate with treasurers for the 'carry-forward' (see below)
     of rights to non-recurring expenditure (e.g. an equipment purchase
     which would not otherwise be possible) into a later budget year.

The typical model of managing planned savings and virement discussed
above normally involves the budget holder being allowed to vire up to 100 %
of planned savings in the financial year in which the savings are achieved.
The original budget is then cut in the subsequent years by the amount of the
savings, at least where the savings are from recurring expenditure.

But there is an alternative approach which provides that budgets will not
be cut back in later years, regardless of whether savings are recurring or
non-recurring. Its supporters argue that this alternative approach has
greater motivational impact, even though they would limit the portion of
any budget underspendings or savings which may be vired to 50 %. Under
this approach there is a continuing incentive to the budget holder to repeat
the level of savings or underspending achieved, and a continuing benefit
both to the budget holder (who redeploys 50 %) and to the health authority
(which regains the other 50 % of the savings to central funds). This
approach has been used successfully with nurse managers of ward budgets
in Manchester.

*Carry-forward*

**4.15**   Health authority overspendings are carried forward to be deducted as a first charge against the next year's allocations. This same rule is normally repeated within authorities in respect of individual budgets which may have been overspent without exceptional justification and advance agreement. In the case of underspendings, authorities may normally carry forward up to 1 % of revenue funding, and up to 10 % of captial funding, for addition to the following year's allocations.

Sometimes even higher levels of carry-forward (and/of-virement between revenue and capital) may be allowable with region and DHSS approval, at least if related to the funding of priority strategic schemes such as the opening of a new district general hospital (DGH) or the planned transfer of resources from long-stay institutions to facilities for community care. This flexibility can be important in assisting the process of financial management for strategic change discussed in Chapter 10.

**4.16** At the level of the budget holder within an authority, it appears to be rare for any automatic rights of carry-forward of underspending to be granted, although presumably carry-forward is possible in deserving cases and if the authority's overall financial position permits, after negotiation. Treasurers often argue that within an authority the underspendings of some budget holders are usually roughly cancelled out by the overspendings of other budget holders, so that automatic rights of carry-forward would not be in the overall interest of the authority.

There is logic in this, but there is also the opposing argument that lack of carry-forward facilities may encourage budget holders to spend money hastily and perhaps unwisely at the end of the budget year if they find that fortuitous savings (which they cannot convert into virement) are leading to underspending. This problem was considered critically in the research for the Royal Commission in the context of the end-of-year spending spree that was then considered to exist. Indeed this probably still exists, but on a much lesser scale owing to lower rates of annual growth in funding together with real improvements in the quality of monitoring and reporting budget holders' expenditure compared to budget. Whether more should or can be done to give budget holders greater incentives to seek and find planned savings is a matter for wider debate.

*Incentives and sanctions*

**4.17** Superficially there would appear to be no great need for budgetary spending sanctions in the NHS. The NHS as a whole has overspent significantly only in one year since cash limits began in 1976. Regions normally balance out small over-and underspendings amongst themselves. Regions also assist districts to largely balance out. Few districts overspend markedly. Within districts there is seldom pronounced overspending by individual budget holders: management monitoring and peer-group pressure usually keeps this within bounds. But visible overspending may only be the tip of the iceberg. The problem is that we can never be sure that authorized budgets are not sometimes higher than needful in the first place, so that the absence of overspending of itself gives no proof that spending was not higher than needed, and therefore too high.

**4.18** It is of course not easy to challenge budget levels proposed or defended by responsible budget-holder managers who are experts in their own fields. Nevertheless the increased use of detailed performance indicators in comparative analysis may assist such challenges, although two main arguments may often be invoked to defend established budgets. The first argument is that case mix and other service characteristics are never fully or even highly comparable between different authorities. Even if that argument can be disproven, there is the second argument that many if not most functional budget holders are not in control of their volume of activity or even, in some cases (e.g. pharmacy), in control of the costliness of their consumables or their processes. Rather, it is argued, it is the decisions of doctors which determine these matters. And this, of course, is a major factor in the view that clinicians must be brought more deeply and effectively into roles in budgeting and financial management at unit and district level. Chapter 7 deals with this issue at length, with particular concern for the financial aspects of the Griffiths Inquiry Report.

**4.19** Regardless of the future involvement of clinicians in financial control, unit management groups and individual functional managers and budget holders will continue to have a major impact on the economy, efficiency and effectiveness of the use of NHS resources. So there is a case for improving the motivation of all budget holders to seek improved performance (not forgetting the quality-of-output dimension to this). Here there are at least two schools of thought. One holds that there is a positive need for incentives (i.e. 'carrots') to induce budget holders and managers to seek savings. Here virement seems the most obvious vehicle, as the opportunity to economize in some routine category of expenditure and as a reward receive a virement to expend part or all of the same funds on a non-recurring expenditure of greater interest (e.g. new equipment) or sometimes even on new recurring expenditure (e.g. staffing for a new computer and information system), is argued to be a powerful incentive.

**4.20** A second school of thought holds that the above approach is risky. There is concern that budget holders might sometimes switch resources from services which may be unglamourous but nevertheless important to standards of patient care or patients' perceptions of the care they are receiving, in favour of one-off non-recurring expenditure on, for example, new equipment which, however worthy, will not really exceed the opportunity cost of the patient services permanently cut back. This school of thought would prefer not to emphasize incentives such as the planned savings and virement exercise, but rather would emphasize the educating of clinicians and managers in financial and economic issues and analysis, combined with involving both these groups more fully in operational planning – the hope being that this will lead to a more optimal choice and use of scarce resources, with a better balance of care resulting than would arise from simply promoting piecemeal cost-improvement incentives. It is certainly true that it will gradually become harder to identify tolerable expenditure savings which do not reduce service standards as bases for the virement incentives, so that eventually the motivational impact of virement incentives may be severely blunted.

An independent view might be that both schools of thought have considerable merit, and that the advice of both should be followed simultaneously. After all, it will take some years before all clinicians and service managers can be educated sufficiently in financial and economic analysis to have a substantial impact on their behaviour as planners and resource managers. Meanwhile, early progress is possible by well organized and publicized incentive savings schemes.

*Reserves*

**4.21** At the time of the Royal Commission's research there was evidence that treasurers held excessive reserves (i.e. that part of funding allocations which is not reallocated initially to specific budgets, but is instead held centrally). At that time the cash limits system was new, funding allocations were often announced late or were altered, the inflation rate was erratic, and the functional budgeting system was new and unproven. In such circumstances it is not surprising that treasurers sought to hold substantial central reserves against contingencies. Sometimes these reserves were excessive, and their release and distribution late in the financial year to budget holders contributed to 'annual spending sprees'.

By now, of course, one may hope that the above four arguments for holding substantial reserves are no longer valid. An unfortunate byproduct of holding excessive central reserves is that budget holders may believe that their own overspending can be 'bailed out' by pleading for a share of these reserves. Presumably most treasurers have successfully overcome this problem and now hold only very small reserves centrally, typically covering only pay and prices inflation (which elements are added to the operational budgets in instalments as these higher costs actually arise) and the budgeted costs of planned new developments starting after the beginning of the financial year, for which adequate resources must be 'held in trust'. In general, there is no obvious case for holding any other kinds of reserves centrally, and it appears that most treasurers accept, in the spirit of the 1982 reorganization with its emphasis on creating strong units of management, that all available funds should be made available to units at the budget planning stage, for them to budget at that time in the most effective way possible.

# Other approaches to budgeting

*Budgeting and management decentralization*

**4.22** A criticism of NHS functional budgeting in its early years was that responsibility for budgets, and for decisions on commitments against budgets and on any savings or virements to seek, was held at too high a level of district management. Budget managers at more junior levels were not given sufficient delegated discretion over budgets to encourage them to feel and behave responsibly as accountable resources managers. Since the 1982 reorganization districts have been expected to decentralize budgetary responsibility to unit level, and it is to be hoped that enlightened unit general managers will ensure that their own managers (department heads, nursing officers, or in future perhaps clinicians) will be given genuine discretion, initiative and responsibility for planning and managing budgets.

Sometimes close monitoring, reporting and inquiry into budgetary performance is seen as interference from the centre. This is a misunderstanding. It is a precept of good management in all types of organizations that effective budgetary control to ensure that resource limits are not being exceeded and that key policy areas, such as manpower limits, are on course, is a prerequisite or indeed an enabling instrument to allow higher tiers of management to withdraw from meddling in the details of operational decisions, so that operational managers can get on with the job of achieving the best output possible within the financial resources available, as guided by their professional and managerial experience.

### Budget holders/managers/monitors

**4.23**   The terminology of 'budget holders' and 'budget managers' widely used in the NHS is inimical to implementing desirable role relationships in budgeting under management decentralization. Anyone who manages a budget should be the budget holder for that budget – that is, s/he should be the primary focus of accountability for budgetary performance, and for related forward planning and scrutiny for savings or possible virements.

The role of those at more senior levels now commonly termed 'budget holders' would be more aptly rechristened 'budget monitors': this would describe the normal, ongoing role relationship at senior level. This in no way denies these senior managers either the right or the responsibility to intervene if monitoring indicates unacceptable performance by subordinates, or the right to take part actively in the more strategic aspects of forward planning of budgets, as ring-holder for the balancing of resources between the needs of all budget holders within a particular unit, function or department.

### Programme budgeting

**4.24**   Programme budgeting is a generic term covering a number of techniques for organizing the planning, funding and monitoring of activities or objectives which transcend single functions or single lines of managerial authority and accountability. Within the NHS this approach can be related to planning and budgeting for care groups: for example the care of the elderly is fragmented between the community and different hospital specialties, and in particular any shift of resources for the care of the elderly to the community obviously needs co-ordinated planning. Programme budgeting can also be used for co-ordinating resource requirements and transfers for a major development such as a new DGH.

However, programme budgeting is not suitable for budgetary control of current expenditure because it does not relate financial accountability to any one individual or to a cohesive team, an essential requirement in financial and managerial discipline. So programme budgeting is not an alternative to conventional budgeting. Indeed 'programme planning' would probably be a better label for its proper role: it can contribute to forward planning to the stage of influencing the level of budget allocation for the coming year to various departments or functions which must be co-ordinated to achieve programme objectives. Once the budget year starts, however, financial control must be achieved through the established operational budgets.

## Zero-base budgeting

**4.25** As previously stated, the antithesis of incremental budgeting is zero-base budgeting (ZBB), first given publicity through its adoption by Governor Jimmy Carter in Georgia. The principal of ZBB is simple and straightforward: the continuation of no existing activity is guaranteed, and each activity should stand the test of inquiry as to whether or not it should continue, at what scale, and with what level of expenditure. In its pure form, ZBB inquiry would take place at the start of each year's budget planning cycle.

The problems with all this, in an NHS context, are, first that it is inconceivable that most of the activities of the NHS could be abolished or even greatly reduced in scale, and secondly that the volume of staff time and supporting information required for rigorous annual ZBB appraisals of the performance and needs of each and every NHS department and service would be excessively expensive of scarce finance, planning and internal audit staff.

**4.26** Nevertheless, the state of mind and approach to performance review embodied in ZBB can be valuable. Many treasurers are considering how to include the ZBB approach within NHS budgetary reviews. One way would be to hold major reviews of performance, value for money and resource needs for all activities, assessed simultaneously and repeated at intervals of three to five years. Another way would be to review a fraction of the authority's activities each year, covering all activities over a three to five-year cycle, although there is bound to be some loss of impact if all inter-relating activities and the opportunity costs of their respective resource needs cannot be reviewed, and balanced, simultaneously.

Any ZBB review needs very substantial advance preparation, and part of the art appears to lie in identifying relevant groupings (or 'packages') of outputs and of the resource inputs consumed. There is an extensive literature for guidance on this, and management consultants are most willing to advise on particular systems for tackling ZBB reviews.

## Management by objectives

**4.27** Management by objectives (MBO) is sometimes described as an approach or method of budgeting, but this is not its traditional role as pioneered by John Humble and others. Rather MBO was seen as a quite independent exercise, compensating for some of the weaknesses of budgeting systems. This approach to MBO starts with the premise that managers cannot focus simultaneously on all the objectives or performance criteria relevant to their jobs and reflected indirectly in budgets, and also that annual budget cycles are too lengthy a period over which to measure progress to objectives.

**4.28** Classical MBO has a number of characteristics. First it should take the form of an agreement between a manager and his boss that the manager should undertake to improve performance relevant to agreed objectives, with success in this undertaking to be reviewed at the end of an agreed period, say six months. The performance criteria chosen must be few in number, objective and measurable (e.g. length of time on waiting list before admission, percentage of X-rays or tests which have to be redone, amount of food waste, energy consumption relative to temperature). There must be a member of staff responsible for MBO schemes, who ensures that MBO agreements are made, that information for monitoring progress is made available, and that at the end of each exercise managers and their bosses meet to review the degree of progress achieved, and perhaps to agree on a further round of MBO activity.

For better or worse, there is little evidence that many British organizations use formalized MBO procedures as described, and of course it is possible to argue that MBO is simply a formalization of what effective bosses should anyway be doing continuously in setting challenges for, and monitoring performance by, their subordinate managers. But it is unknown how many bosses live up to this model!

## Budgeting: money and workload

**4.29** This chapter has been about the principles and practices of good budgeting, set in an NHS context. The essential minimum characteristics of a budgeting system are that it distributes authorization to spend money, on resources, and that it monitors, reports and controls the expenditure out-turn which follows. But all of this gives no clue as to managerial perfor-mance in achieving value for money. Does underspending a budget provide evidence of economy? Does balancing a budget 'spot-on' indicate effi-ciency? Do planned savings achieved in manpower, with virement of the savings into the purchase of new technology equipment, suggest effective-ness? An instinctive answer to all these questions is 'yes', but alas budgetary data alone cannot answer the questions at all meaningfully.

**4.30** If we are to seek useful answers to the above questions, then we must have matching data on the output or workload achieved with the input of physical resources represented by the financial budgets expended. We must know, for example, how many meals were provided for a given level of budgetary expenditure on catering, i.e. so as to determine what is the average cost per meal. And even the latter figure proves nothing. To progress further we must have one or more comparators, for example, the budgeted average cost per meal, last year's actual cost per meal (adjusted for inflation), costs in a comparable hospital or district, or a standard cost or 'norm' cost derived from expert assessment.

Comparing one or more of these costs with the local actual cost per meal will provide insight into economy and efficiency, but not into effectiveness. And the insight will not be conclusive. To strengthen the conclusions we would need further data on the wholesomeness, palatability and suitability of meals served relative to patient needs and wishes, especially if we are seriously to attempt to evaluate effectiveness.

At the present stage of evolution of NHS information it would be unrealistic to expect all of the above data to be brought together to assess economy and efficiency, let alone effectiveness, on any routine, continuing basis of reporting and monitoring. On the other hand, even at the present state of the art and of available information we could require occasional studies covering all of the above factors as part of a programme of periodic, in-depth reviews of performance such as might be conducted under some modified programme based on ZBB or similar performance review principles.

**4.31** The work of the (Körner) NHS/DHSS Steering Group on Health Services Information has broadly progressed on three parallel fronts – activity, financial and manpower information. Activity information is the measurement of outputs, throughputs or workloads. These are intermediate measures of progress towards NHS objectives, which are successful health outcomes. Financial information and manpower information are both measures of inputs. Financial information covers all the inputs, including the monetary value of manpower. Manpower constitutes 70–5% of total revenue costs in most health districts, the figure being nearer the bottom end of this range in teaching districts and nearer the upper end in non-teaching districts.

Manpower information is of obvious importance for personnel management. However, personnel information is not of great importance in financial management to the extent that good budgetary and other financial information systems anyway include and report the payroll costs of the use of manpower. Financial budget allocations, and rigorous monitoring and control of these, are almost certainly the best regulators of the level of manpower costs in the NHS. Certainly the percentage of total budget expenditure incurred for payroll should be closely monitored, especially in districts with nil growth in funding or with contraction. Any increase in the percentage of total spending going on payroll, after adjusting for the timing of annual pay rises, should be seen as a warning signal that supplies, equipment and maintenance may be being run down to compensate for the costs of retaining more manpower than justified by the current level of total revenue funding. That is, it is wasteful to retain manpower (e.g. by refilling vacancies) if there are not sufficient drugs, prosthetics, efficient equipment, etc., to keep doctors, nurses and support staff fully occupied in treating patients.

**4.32** The essential point to emerge from this chapter is that levels of budget authorization and expenditure have very little significance in themselves, beyond the need for each authority to balance its books within its cash limits. Conformity to budgets in no way gives assurance that services have been delivered economically, efficiently or effectively. In order to monitor the latter objectives we must have relevant and accurate activity information to set beside budgetary, costing and other financial information.

As we shall consider in more detail in chapters dealing with specialty costing and clinical budgeting, it is widely recognized that the greatest need for rapid improvement in NHS information for management control is in the area of accurate, timely information on the level of activity/ workload/output of service departments, wards, theatres and clinics, etc. Given such improvement, which will involve both a more disciplined collection of data and its computerization for economical and speedy analysis, the quality of budgetary control can be improved substantially, and thus the value of its contribution to the better management of health authorities.

In the next chapter we consider the problems of costing and budgeting in the aftermath of the 1982 reorganization, with the need to co-ordinate the established functional management accountability with the new dimension of unit management responsibility.

## Summary

1 Budgets are more than just funding allocations. They are, or should be, costed plans indicating allowable resources (money, man-power, space, equipment, etc.) to meet an estimated or targeted workload.

2 Old-fashioned 'incremental budgets' where last year's spend becomes the baseline for the next year's budget (to which are added automatic formula increases for inflation and average growth) should no longer occur. All budgets should be negotiated with budget holders, in the light of workload plans and changes in methods of treatment.

3 'Flexed budgets' can be used so the budgeted variable costs (usually mainly consumables) can go up or down in response to variations from the planned workload.

4 Budgetary control works only if there is regular monthly reporting of accurate activity/workload and cost performance figures. Reports should be prompt, understandable, and followed up by personal contact from the general manager or his adviser whenever any spending or workload problems appear.

5 Every unit should have a unit financial adviser or management accountant to maintain continuing contact with all budget holders regarding their budget performance, workloads and forward planning for cost improvements, redeployment of resources, etc.

6 Effective budgeting needs built-in incentives to encourage budget holders to seek planned savings, and sanctions against budget holders who underperform or who overspend without first negotiating over the need and the availability of resources. Negotiated virement and carry-forward are means of making budgetary control more flexible to meet needs.

7 Carefully negotiated budgets and close monitoring and follow-up of budgetary performance are an important means by which general managers can increase delegation, or decentralization, without loss or overall co-ordination and responsibility.

8 Zero-base budgeting is a technique to challenge budget holders to justify their current range and volume of activity and cost. Management by objectives is a technique for helping managers improve performance by focusing on measurable portions of their workload or resource use, one manageable portion at a time.

9 Budget systems for effective performance monitoring and control must be supported by accurate, reliable and prompt flows of costed activity and workload data from all patient treatment services.

# CHAPTER 5
# Budgeting and accountability in unit management

**5.1**  Previous chapters introduced the need for better financial information and control in the NHS, and explained the main terminology and concepts of costing and budgeting in an NHS context. This chapter considers the system of costing and budgeting currently available throughout the NHS in the context of the new unit structures from the 1982 reorganization. It also considers issues of organization and decentralization which may assist the improvement of unit management in the spirit of the 1982 reorganization and of the Griffiths general manager role. Chapters 6, 7 and 8 then look forward to the improved financial information to be introduced as the result of Körner, Griffiths and a few other major initiatives, which should assist the growing involvement of clinicians in cost evaluation and in budget-planning choices of the best use of scarce resources, i.e. what is now called 'resource management'.

## Background to the 1982 reorganization

*Subjective and functional costs and budgets*

**5.2**  Prior to the 1974 reorganization the main cost accounting and reporting system in the NHS was based on 'subjective costing', i.e. a breakdown of what kinds of goods, services and pay money was expended for. Budgeting, such as it was, was little more than a process of estimation of what each of these headings would cost in the next year after allowing for new developments, followed by a monitoring of the outturn. In many cases these subjective costs and budgets were not clearly identifiable to the managerial responsibility of any one person.

**5.3**  A major managerial feature of the 1974 reorganization was the emphasis given to the upgrading of the status and responsibility of 'functional' organization and management. Here 'functional' very largely signified 'professional' or 'discipline based', and the new functional organization structure with hierarchical lines of accountability to district level within each function helped to enlarge the role and status of individual professions, perhaps most notably nursing.

The arrangements for management responsibility brought in with the

1974 reorganization stressed the importance of establishing budgets and financial control based on functional control and accountability right up to district management level. This was achieved by coding and classifying the subjective costs by functional category.

The largest single functional budget was for nursing, and often this was managed as though the district nursing officer was the only 'budget holder' for nursing, with sector or other lower tier nursing officers perceived as delegated 'budget managers' having little discretion of their own in budget planning or virement, their role being seen as essentially that of agents on behalf of the district level budget holder.

**5.4** Both 'subjective' and 'functional' cost and budgeting systems are orientated to 'inputs' and the control of inputs. And yet, to continue our nursing example, functional costing and budgeting did not succeed in bringing together in one total *all* the input costs of the nursing activity, which itself comprises an important 'output' of caring service. Typically nursing budgets have included only nursing pay, overtime, study leave, recruitment, training and nursing administration support costs. These budgets have excluded the costs of ward consumables, and catering and laundry services, etc., for the reason that the latter have come under the responsibility of some other functional management department head.

Thus the effect of functional costing and budgeting was to reflect and possibly even to exacerbate a splintered perspective of resource use and responsibility, with integration of information and review of resource needs and the marginal benefits of altering the balance of resource use largely occurring only at district level, remote from the 'sharp end' of patient treatment.

**5.5** The expanded analysis of nursing costs to include consumables and services controlled or at least influenced by nurses is called 'ward costing'. There have been successful developments in ward costing and budgeting, but we will leave discussion until later for the reasons that the present chapter is concerned only with information systems immediately available in all districts, and that ward costing is anyway perhaps most usefully viewed as but one component of the general improvement of costing needed on an integrated basis to achieve specialty costing (and ultimately to achieve specialty or clinical budgeting).

**5.6** The effect of the 1982 reorganization in moving the level of integration and review of functional budgets to unit management level offers scope for improved performance in the tactical, short-term use of resources. The appointment of unit general managers should reinforce the integration of functions, given clinical support, and this should help to switch the focus of attention from the functional rationing of inputs to the balancing of inputs for maximizing outputs within global budget limits.

## Unit management budgets

**5.7** At the time of the 1982 reorganization treasurers had to draw up new standing financial instructions for approval and adoption by the new district health authorities. Then, as new unit management arrangements were agreed, treasurers had additionally to prepare statements on budgetary policy and guidelines for managers on the operation of budgetary planning and control.

It may be helpful to review an example of such guidelines. Here bear in mind the cardinal principle that budgets and the rules governing their operation must faithfully mirror the intended organization structure and division of tasks, authority and responsibility between the different tiers and functions of management. While assembling information for the writing of this book the author was kindly sent by treasurers various examples of budgetary guidelines. Some of these have been quite impressive, such as the very detailed booklet provided by East Dorset Health Authority. But we have space here to reproduce only a briefer set of guidelines, and indeed brevity can be a virtue in making it more likely that rules will actually be read and understood, while offering fewer hostages to fortune through over-prescription.

The example below, prepared in April 1983 by Mr C.J. Savory when Treasurer of Ealing Health Authority, is not only concise but also clearly captures the spirit of the 1982 reorganization – namely, that once operational plans and budgets have been agreed then units should be left with maximum discretion to deploy their financial resources to best advantage.

# Delegation of budgets and financial discretion to unit level

## 1. Introduction

1.1 Circular HC(80)8 – Structure and Management – urges the early establishment of unit budgets, as 'an essential element in increasing local responsibility and accountability' (Paragraph 30). Such budgets should operate within financial allocations and policies for virement between and within units of management as set by the Authority.

1.2 Paragraph 33 of HC(80)8 states that Regional Health Authorities should assist DHAs in developing adequate financial systems and budgetary control procedures at and within Districts. Subject to this, DHAs will be free to exercise their financial responsibilities, with budget control and cash limit arrangements providing for the maximum local delegation consistent with overall control of the DHA Cash Limit. District Treasurers are also expected to provide financial advice as necessary to the budget holder at unit level through improved financial information systems.

1.3 This paper therefore makes proposals for delegating financial discretion to unit management following agreement on the Authority's management arrangements.

## 2. Management arrangements

2.1 As required by Paragraph 27 of HC(80)8, the Authority has arranged its services into four units of management as follows:

(i)    *Community unit*

    (ii)   *Mental health unit*
    (iii)  *Acute unit*
    (iv)  *Maternity unit*

2.2  In addition to the four units of management, the Authority has agreed to retaining and/or creating certain functions at District Headquarters.

2.3  The key principle underlying the proposals set out in this paper is that budgetary responsibilities both flow from, and are an integral part of, management arrangements.

2.4  The Authority has issued Standing Financial Instructions which provide for the regulation and conduct of its financial affairs. Section II of these Instructions covers the requirements of estimates, the preparation and approval of budgets and the exercise of budgetary control, both by individual budget holders and by the District Management Team.

2.5  The Authority's Standing Financial Instructions place a clear duty on the Treasurer to devise and maintain systems of budgetary control which shall incorporate the reporting of, and investigation into, expenditure variances from budget as well as the providing of budgetary information and advice to enable officers to carry out their budgetary responsibilities.

2.6  In addition to the responsibilities placed on the Treasurer, the Authority, through its Standing Financial Instructions, places collective responsibility on the District Management Team to carry out its functions within the limits of the overall budgets approved by the Authority, as well as ensuring that financial resources are managed effectively and efficiently.

2.7  The Authority has empowered the District Management Team to delegate responsibility for a budget or part of a budget to an individual officer or group of officers to permit the performance of defined activities. Such delegation of budgetary responsibility must operate within limits approved by the Authority. The terms of such delegation must include a clear definition of individual and group responsibilities for control of expenditure, exercise of virement, achievement of planned levels of service and the provision of regular reports upon the discharge of such delegated functions to the Team. Responsibility for overall budgetary control, however, ramains with the District Management Team and delegated budget holders shall strictly observe any budgetary limits and control procedures defined by the DMT.

2.8  The Authority has also instructed the District Management Team to monitor the use of delegated budgets to ensure that financial control is maintained and that the Authority's plans and policies are implemented.

## 3. *Budgeting at Unit Level*

3.1  Budgeting arrangements at unit level will be geared to the encouragement of maximum delegation to act on operational matters with maximum accountability for decisions taken. Such delegation will operate within policies prescribed by the District Management Team and the Authority.

3.2  Unit budgets will be set, and expenditure monitored, on an *income and expenditure basis*, i.e. as expenditure is *incurred* on goods and services (not when actually paid for). The same principle will apply to income.

3.3  The designation of budget holders is a key feature in achieving effective control of expenditure. Responsibility for budgets will be delegated to the lowest level within the organization compatible with the need to maintain:

    (i)    effective communication
    (ii)   effective accountability.

3.4 There are a number of factors involved in the meaningful designation of budget holders. It is vitally important that budgets should be under the control of an individual officer directly responsible for the management of a particular service. Budget holders will be responsible to their Senior Officer, if appropriate, or direct to the District Management Team for the performance of their budgetary responsibility.

3.5 Paragraph 30 of HC(80)8 states that the unit nurse should be given responsibility for the control of the nursing budget (allocated as part of the district nursing budget) and the unit administrator should control the budgets for departments for which he is managerially responsible and should also be responsible for the co-ordination of other budgets.

This paragraph also requires that these two unit officers should exercise their financial responsibilities within financial allocations and policies for virement between and within units set by the Authority, and also in conjunction with a senior member of the medical staff.

3.6 Whilst it is a fairly straightforward task to designate budget holders for many unit functions/activities, problems arise in relation to certain activities, particularly those of a direct patient care nature, e.g. drugs, medical and surgical supplies and equipment. In addition, it is necessary to recognize that certain departments, e.g. pathology, radiology, provide a service on a District-wide basis.

3.7 In theory, at least, it is possible to institute a budgetary control system for direct patient care budgets based on 'Cogwheel' divisions or even individual clinicians. For such a system to opearate successfully two essential conditions are required. Firstly, it is necessary to have a well-developed sophisticated information system relating to the consumption of resources. Secondly, it is absolutely vital that clinicians, both individually and collectively, are prepared to participate in such arrangements.

## 4. Proposed Virement Powers

4.1 A key component to achieving real delegation of financial discretion to units is the ability to manage money on a flexible basis. Thus, the rules governing the switching of funds from one heading to another, i.e. exercising virement, is one of the most important decisions the Authority can take. Clearly, virement powers cannot be unlimited, otherwise the initial decisions taken by the Authority and the District Management Team could be completely nullified. On the other hand if virement powers are too restrictive it will not allow the unit the freedom to manage, which is the keynote of Reorganization.

4.2 The following are therefore put forward as a set of principles for consideration by the Authority:

1. Any virement is allowed except where expressly excluded below.
2. Virement proposals *must* be considered within a Unit context (including proposals between Units).
3. No virement from a *non*-recurring saving to a recurring purpose.
4. No virement may exceed £10,000 or 2% of the budget, whichever is the greater, without the prior approval of the District Management Team.
5. Fortuitous savings are at the disposal of budget holders in exactly the same way as planned savings. Conversely budget holders must recognize that unplanned overspends, regardless of cause, will be expected to be recovered by budget holders.
6. No virement can be deemed to have taken place until both budget holders have confirmed their agreement *in writing* to the Treasurer and had the

proposed change to their budgets confirmed. In addition, it will be necessary for any budget holder initiating a request for virement, to demonstrate that due consideration has been given to possible implications on other functions within the unit.

7. The District Management Team may, on occasions, require virement across units.
8. No virement is possible between revenue and capital (or vice versa) without the prior approval of the District Management Team.

## 5. *Reserves*

5.1 The holding of reserves at District level runs counter to the policy of delegation. It is therefore proposed to hold *no* reserves at District.
5.2 The Authority receives an allowance to cover pay and price increases during each financial year. Inflation is a phenomenon from which until recently Health Authorities have, to a very large extent, been protected. However with the introduction of cash planning it would seem appropriate to allocate the available funds at the beginning of the financial year and budget holders will be expected to contain spending within budget.

# Annex: Proposed budgetary responsibilities

## 1. *The District Management Team*

The Team's financial/budgetary responsibilities include:

(a) advice to the Authority on management structures, delegation, accountability and monitoring procedures;
(b) maintenance of approved policies and procedures;
(c) advice to the Authority on the sharing of resources between competing demands;
(d) setting performance targets;
(e) monitoring performance in terms of cost effectiveness and available resources to ensure that total expenditure is contained within the level approved by the Authority;
(f) advice and assistance to Unit Management Groups in relation to management of resources.

## 2. *The Unit Management Group*

The Group's budgetary responsibilities include:

(a) participation in the budget/performance target setting procedure for the Unit and the various activities within the Unit;
(b) monitoring performance in budgetary, cost and workload terms to ensure that the Unit as a whole is operating efficiently within its overall financial allocation;
(c) examining trends in activity and cost levels and taking steps to ensure that these are contained within the resources actually allocated to the Unit;
(d) the motivation of all staff in a common effort to make the best use of the limited resources available in the interests of the patient;
(e) instructing Budget Holders to take specific action to reduce expenditure either to avoid an overspending on an individual budget, a hospital budget or the aggregate budget for the Unit.

## 3. The Budget Holder

The Budget Holder is responsible for:

(a) control of staffing levels including sickness, overtime and other allowance, which are expressed in budget reports in whole-time equivalents (w.t.e.) within the funded establishment or such other level as may be authorized/required temporarily by the Unit Management Group;

(b) control of expenditure on non-staff items which are controllable and to influence those who create the need for expenditure on other items within the budget by their demand for service;

(c) provision of an agreed quantity and quality of service within a fixed level of resources (wherever possible quantity will be expressed in workload terms so that cost/efficiency can be monitored);

(d) identification of future changes in technology or demand for the services provided which may lead to changes ( + or – ) in the level of resources required;

(e) action necessary to maintain total costs within the annual budget, after consultation and agreement with the Unit Management Group or DMT (as appropriate) where this involves a reduction in quantity or quality of service;

(f) constant review of working methods and the use of equipment and consumables to identify ways of achieving better value for money.

## 4. The Treasurer's Department

The District Treasurer is the financial adviser to the Authority, the DMT and Chief Officers. His department provides financial services (payroll, payment of invoices, collection of income, accounting services) and budgetary services to all disciplines. The main point of contact for the majority of budget holders will be with designated management accountants who work with the Unit Managers. In addition to providing financial advice to the Unit Managers, the Management Accountant will provide an advisory/information service to all budget holders to help them manage their budgets and particularly to encourage them to identify ways of using the resources at their disposal more effectively.

The principal budgetary responsibilities of the Management Accountant are:

(a) preparation of annual budgets and supporting documentation in close liaison with the budget holder;

(b) update budgets during the year for increases in the allocation for pay and prices;

(c) ensure that expenditure is correctly analysed and charged to the proper budget heading;

(d) produce monthly statements of performance against budget, comment on variances in manpower levels, expenditure and workload, and assist the budget holder in the identification of the reasons for such variances;

(e) assist the budget holder in obtaining better value for money with the resources available;

(f) assist the budget holder in identifying expenditure/workload trends which may lead to changes ( + or – ) in the level of resources required;

(g) produce summary reports and comments for the function/hospital/Unit as necessary and to advise the appropriate level of management;

(h) attend meetings of Unit Managers to advice on the overall budgetary situation and participate in group decisions on matters which have financial implications;

(i) produce financial reports on the Units' performance for the District Treasurer as required;

(j) ensure adherence to the budgetary policies and procedures approved by the DMT and/or the DHA.

## Comments on the Savory paper

**5.8** This section reviews matters arising from the 1983 Savory paper (cross-referencing is by mention of paragraph numbers in the Savory paper). Paragraph 2.1 indicates that the district's new units were only four in number, and were based on separate client groups. These characteristics make it easier to operate a high degree of managerial/budgetary delegation to units, as compared to some districts where much larger populations and geographic areas, and a larger number of acute hospitals, have made it apparently desirable to provide two or more acute units and/or community units, with need for district management to remain more managerially involved to minimize the risk of uneconomic duplication of facilities or services, or other waste through lack of co-ordination.

**5.9** Paragraphs 2.6 and 2.8 lend emphasis to the point that budgetary discipline is a collective responsibility of the entire district management team (as distinct from just the treasurer alone). It is not presently clear to what extent ultimate budgetary responsibility will be transferred to the district general managers. In any event, strictly, the ultimate responsibility is carried by the health authority itself, as distinct from its officers – even if, in practice, the onus weighs more heavily on the officers' shoulders because the sanctions on them for failure are likely to be much more penal.

**5.10** Paragraph 3.2 refers to the same distinction between accrual and cash-flow accounting made earlier in Chapter 3, paragraph 3.20, of this book. The point is that accrual-based 'income and expenditure accounting' at least partly removes distortions in expenditure patterns caused by accidental and/or intentional variations in the timing of purchases and cash payments, neither of which may match closely with the actual rate at which supplies or other resources are actually consumed.

**5.11** Paragraph 3.3 interprets a major objective of the 1982 reorganization, to encourage decentralization of decision-making and accountability to the lowest managerial level where good performance monitoring and financial control is economically possible. While the sentiments are valid, generalized expressions such as 'the need to maintain: (i) effective communication and (ii) effective accountability' still leave much scope for differences of interpretation in practice. There may be many ways to improve communication, but an important general point is that communication will be the more effective the fewer the number of levels or tiers of hierarchy there are in an organization. Effective accountability depends greatly on the climate of managerial discipline and commitment, but also it depends crucially on the quality of financial and related information available.

**5.12** Paragraph 3.5 refers to a contentious part of the reorganization circular (HC(80)8) requiring that the unit nursing officer should control the unit nursing budget (allocated from the district nursing budget). There was concern that this aspect of the 1982 reorganization could undermine district-wide leadership and co-ordination of nursing services. This concern became even greater following the Griffiths Inquiry Report in October 1983, as the only logical interpretation of the introduction of 'general management' and the appointment of unit general managers would be that the latter would effectively become the 'ultimate' budget holders for all unit budgets, with heads of functions (such as nursing) within units becoming de facto 'delegated' budget holders. But aside from this paragraph, and possibly paragraph 3.6, the quoted paper on budget arrangements following the 1982 reorganization would need little amendment to reflect the Griffiths' recommendations. In paragraph 3.6 there is reference to the important complication that departments located physically and managerially within a single unit may in practice provide a district-wide service. If 'customer units' are to be held financially accountable, then they must be recharged for their volume of use of such district-wide services.

We shall return to this again in a later chapter: it is part of a wider problem affecting clinical budgeting as well, because of the fact that functional departmental budgets and unit costs frequently do not include *all* the costs of providing a service. For example, radiology department budgets may often fail to include the labour costs of nurses, clerks, porters and technicians contributing to the work of the department, simply because they have been budgeted and costed to the separate functions representing their own professional disciplines.

**5.13**   On the subject of virement powers, paragraph 4.1 states the general problem for any district: that of getting the balance right between a high degree of freedom for unit managements to vire (i.e. transfer) financial resources between one use and another, according to their perceptions of need and opportunity cost, without on the other hand incurring the risk that decisions and plans previously agreed between the unit and the authority or its DMT may be unilaterally nullified.

And yet for the latter extreme result to occur, it could only mean that the unit had been an unwilling partner in the previous planning and decision-making, or else that circumstances had changed. In either of these situations there may be a good case for resources virement, although if the amount of money is large or the impact on previous plans and commitments is major, virement should presumably arise only through negotiation rather than as an automatic right.

**5.14**   The principles for virement put forward in paragraph 4.2 are essentially consistent with maintaining the fine balance referred to above. However, some might argue that limiting automatic virement rights (sub-paragraph 4), to £10,000 or 2% of the budget, whichever is the greater, is too restrictive. This is a matter for judgement, and in practice such judgement presumably will be influenced not just by the temperament and degree of self-confidence of different managements, but also by their circumstances: managements in districts losing resources under RAWP are likely to be more conservative in setting virement limits and in limiting virement of fortuitous savings, regardless of whether or not this is actually the optimal policy for motivating managers when resources are scarce.

The argument over fortuitous savings is especially difficult. One may feel sympathy for virement rights on fortuitous savings arising from an unexpected improvement in efficiency, or perhaps from a favourable price change in some input or even from a genuine inability to fill staff vacancies, whereas one might not feel sympathy in the case of savings resulting from an unplanned reduction in workload, or from a planned improvement in efficiency not disclosed in previous budget bargaining lest original budgets be cut. All this highlights weaknesses in the management information currently available. We do not as yet have sufficiently accurate measures of workload and throughput to enable budget levels to be flexed automatically, for example to provide a fairer baseline for determining if there are funds available for virement.

**5.15** In its paragraph 5.1 the Savory paper suggests that *no* reserves should be held at district, and paragraph 5.2 indicates that the annual pay and prices allowance districts receive to cover government estimates of inflation should be allocated to individual budgets at the beginning of the financial year. Here we may be playing with words, to the extent that the allocation of pay and prices allowance could still be phased over the year according to the estimated timing of increases, without the unspent residue of the early months having to be labelled a 'reserve'. Certainly, spreading pay and prices increments evenly across all the months of a year could be risky, at least if the rate of inflation once again accelerated. And reserves may still be needed to protect revenue funds for new developments starting mid-year, or to provide the kind of 'budget flexing' which may become popular in districts using clinical management budgets (Chapter 7).

**5.16** In paragraph 3 of the Annex to the Savory paper its author sensibly gives pride of place in his list of budget holder responsibilities to the 'control of staffing levels'. This includes the control of whole-time equivalent staff numbers to conform with staffing establishments and plans incorporated in the budgets. The use of information on vacancies, mobility and turnover, and on the extent of incremental creep in salary grades and other staffing characteristics, all give valuable early-warning indicators of expenditure patterns likely to be reflected subsequently in payroll budget outturns.

The quality and comparability of manpower control information is likely to be enhanced over the next few years by wide adoption of the recommendations in the Körner Group's 'Third Report to the Secretary of State' on manpower information. Improved control over absenteeism, overtime and allowances of staff may well be the largest single source of potential savings (and/or productivity gains) remaining to be tapped in the NHS by alert management action.

**5.17** Item (h) of paragraph 4 of the Annex indicates that the management accountant should attend meetings of unit managers to advise on the budgetary situation and 'participate in group decisions on matters which have financial implications'. Some management accountants in this role have been given the additional or alternative title of 'unit financial adviser' to emphasise a change in their role from work mainly in and for the district, to work clearly linked to the interests and needs of the unit to which they are attached.

On occasion this could lead to a conflict of loyalties for finance staff, between the unit's case and the district's case in the difficult decisions which sometimes arise. Where the level of staffing in treasurers' departments permits, there could be merit in the full-time outposting of trained management accountants to work in units alongside unit general managers, with this role firmly differentiated from management accountants working in the district office to provide information and advice for the DMT and the authority.

## Accountability of unit management

**5.18**  Following the 1974 reorganization there was a direct line of functional accountability from the bottom to the top of each health district in respect of the nursing function and of the diverse activities which came under the purview of the district medical officer and the district administrator, respectively. Since 1982 the 'top' of the district has been the health authority, whose members broadly represent the public both as patients and taxpayers. Between 1974 and 1982 this same situation pertained in single district area authorities.

However, the situation was markedly different in multiple district areas, where the authority was only at area level, advised by a management team with strategic and monitoring duties but cut off from the districts where operational management decisions and control were carried out. This separation is probably one of the causes of the apparent failure of the NHS management arrangements between 1974 and 1982. Now it seems possible that the creation of unit managements with decentralized operational autonomy may replicate a similar problem of communication, accountability and co-ordination, if on a smaller scale. The creation of direct links between unit and district general managers could further exacerbate this problem, at least as regards effective accountability to health authorities.

**5.19**  It is not yet clear what the operational role of the typical DMT will be following the appointment of district and unit general managers. One possible scenario is for the DMT to retain the same membership as at present, except for the district general manager (DGM) as an addition or a replacement for one of the other members. But unit general managers (UGMs) will have assumed responsibility for unit level operations in many of the activities for which the DMO, DNO and DA used to be managerially responsible, or at least directly accountable as budget monitors. So for many or most operational activities of the district the lines of operational responsibility *and* budgetary accountability will have contracted to a direct relationship between the unit general managers and the district general manager. Under this scenario (illustrated in Fig. 5.1) the opportunity for direct debate in authority meetings between members and officers directly accountable for unit affairs will have largely evaporated.

**5.20**  An alternative scenario – with much to commend it as regards public accountability via the meetings of the authority – will be for the

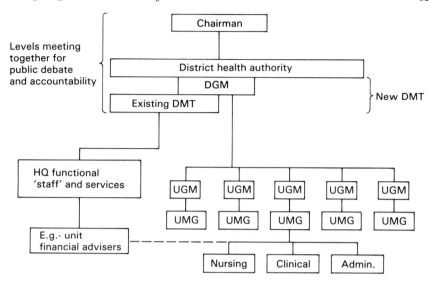

*Fig. 5.1  Simplified example of organization where UGMs are excluded from DMT and shielded from public accountability.*

existing DMT to be enlarged to include all unit general managers additional to the district general manager. This will make for a large DMT but there is ample precedent in the private sector for effective boards of directors which combine the senior *line* executives (i.e. the district and unit general managers) with the *staff* executives responsible for policy review, planning, and central services such as finance (i.e. broadly the functional chief officers).

With such an enlarged DMT (illustrated in Fig. 5.2) there should be a lively and constructive interaction with the health authority, and it should be more easily brought home to unit general managers that they are in post to run a complex service with multiple objectives and a local community to serve and satisfy. Otherwise there is a risk that unit general managers may become too focused on satisfying just the interests and priorities of the staff of their own units, and too reliant on narrow performance criteria relating to cost reduction, or on avoiding conflict with internal pressure groups such as clinicians.

The NHS is not a simple, commercial type of organization which can be adequately monitored by a handful of financial performance indicators – unlike even very large industrial firms – nor is it a closed society which can be allowed to run itself to the self-satisfaction of clinical, managerial, professional or trade union vested-interest groups.

**5.21** The foregoing may seem a provocative if superficial trawl through some of the problems of getting right the organizational accountability relationships between units and their parent districts. Although it was drafted before the decision to appoint unit general managers, *Effective Unit Management* written by staff of the King's Fund College may be commended as excellent reading for a broader view of the problems.

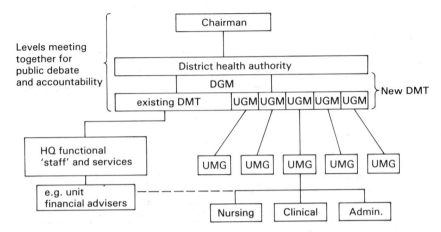

*Fig. 5.2    Simplified example of organization where UGMs are included in DMT and exposed to public accountability.*

**5.22**   An alternative or additional channel for improving financial accountability and the feedback from authority members to unit management is to establish a finance panel of the authority to meet with the DMT and unit general managers to discuss resource planning and financial control issues in depth. A further variation is to establish authority panels linked to each unit – rather like the visiting panels of members often used to liaise with care groups/programmes in the past, or with specific units since 1982. The problem with this latter arrangement, however, is that members may become permanently attached to particular units for which they have some affinity, with the risk that the panels become relatively uncritical pressure groups for 'their' units, whereas what is needed is a critical review of performance and an overview, as objective as possible, of the relative merits and needs of the separate units competing for the resources available. Yet another way in which authority members can be involved in financial performance is through an audit committee. This has been recommended in the Salmon Report.

## Transition

**5.23**   This chapter has been concerned with budgeting and financial control during a period of transition. It has considered the use of post-1974 functional costing and budgeting information during the period of formation of post-1982 unit managements and the further changeover to district and unit general managers more recently. But the presently available financial information is inadequate, so in the next chapter we will consider the introduction of specialty costing, both as recommended by Körner and as needed to facilitate and monitor the clinical management budgeting recommended by Griffiths, as well as the newer and wider concept of 'resource management'.

## Summary

1 The NHS reorganization of 1974 created long, vertical lines of control and accountability within each management function. Functional budgeting matched this organizational arrangement, typically with real budgetary discretion and responsibility only at district level. The 1982 reorganization retained functional organization and functional budgeting, but seemed likely to lead to budgetary power-sharing (or conflict?) between units and districts.

2 The Griffiths general manager innovation from 1984 is supposed to have shifted the focus of budgetary power (over operational as distinct from strategic matters) from the district to the units, although within units functional budgets and costs are still the main system in use unless and until information systems are in place to provide something better. The next stage, with the implementation of Körner reforms, could be budgetary arrangements linked to specialty costing.

3 Unit general managers (with agreement from district treasurers) need to supply their budget holders with clear instructions on how to use budgets, on what are their responsibilities, and what powers of discretion they have in using their budgets (e.g. the virement of funds, the re-use of savings, negotiated carry-forwards, etc.). It should be made clear to budget holders that their discretion will be the greater the more they inform, consult and negotiate with the general manager and his financial adviser. This enables the overall unit budgets and balance of resources to be balanced and co-ordinated.

4 Unless and until clinicians become budget holders accountable for the volume of their workload and the volume of demands they place on service departments existing budget holders remain apparently accountable for costs (e.g. the consumables used in diagnostic tests) they cannot control.

5 Budgets and budgetary performance reports are too important a source of information on problems, trends and planning opportunities to be left to the sole attention of the unit financial adviser. Every unit general manager should become actively involved in using this tool of management.

6 Budgetary control systems match organizational structures. For unit budgets to be effectively decentralised, and co-ordinated and disciplined at unit level, it is probably essential that the unit, through its UGM, is actively represented in decision-making at the 'top of the district'. Thus UGMs preferably should be full members of the district management team, including attendance and participation in health authority meetings and all other fora influencing district policy on financial and resource-use issues.

# CHAPTER 6
# Specialty costing

**6.1** Within health districts we have seen how costing (and budgeting) developed form 1974 to reflect the functional organization structure and the accountability of functional managers for the control of expenditure. Then, with the 1982 reorganization, the authority and initial accountability for decisions on resource use were required to be delegated to unit management groups and their senior functional managers. But that still left the problem that the rate of consumption of available resources is determined more by the decisions of clinicians than by unit management. Indeed there has long been interest in extending cost analysis down to the level of detail of the work of clinicians, the ultimate decision-makers of the end use of the resources provided.

The difficulties in achieving this have comprised the complexity and expense of extra clerical effort in tracing expenditure costs down to the detailed level of clinical activity, and concern that if cost and workload information was not actively used in operational management (as distinct from research and planning) then there would be disinterest in collecting and recording this information such as would jeopardise its accuracy, credibility and value. In recent years, however, there has been growing interest in obtaining and using this extra dimension of information (see 4.9 to 4.11, and Fig. 4.1 in Chapter 4).

**6.2** Clinical costing may be conducted at the level of the specialty, the 'firm' (of doctors working together within a specialty), the individual clinician, or the individual patient or groups of patients with similar characteristics. The latter alternative we leave for detailed discussion in Chapter 9. This chapter concentrates on cost measurement and reporting for clinical activity: this is normally termed 'specialty costing'. However, the same methods of cost and activity recording and analysis may be used to subdivide the information by firm, or by individual clinician if desired, provided that the appropriate degree of detail in 'coding' the recording of resource utilization is employed.

There are three approaches to specialty costing: this chapter explains in turn the 'statistical' approach, the 'sampling' approach and the 'continuous' approach. But first, the Körner Steering Group on Health Services Information has been a leading supporter of specialty costing, and this seems an appropriate point in this book at which to introduce that part of the work of the Körner programme which directly affects NHS financial information, management and control.

## Körner Report on NHS financial information

**6.3** Over the years a sequence of reports were critical of the quality and use made of financial and activity statistics in the NHS. Many of these criticisms were detailed in the reports of the Resource Allocation Working Party, in the 1978 Perrin Report to the Royal Commission and in the Royal Commission's main report of 1979. All this created a supportive climate for the establishment of the NHS/DHSS Steering Group on Health Services Information in 1980, under the distinguished chairmanship of Mrs Edith Körner. The Körner Steering Group quite soon established several working groups to explore specialized areas in some depth, and to submit interim reports. These were followed in each case by consultation, field testing of recommendations in at least four health districts, and the distillation of findings into concise final reports to the Secretary of State.

The working groups and reports may be subdivided into three main categories. These comprise:

a   financial information (our main concern in this book);
b   manpower information (manpower is the NHS's most important resource and consumes nearly 75% of its expenditure); and
c   services activity information for hospitals, community and supporting services.

The latter information has wide-ranging interest for epidemiological, planning and other service applications – but additionally it is indispensable for accurate specialty costing (and also for clinical budgeting or patient costing). This is because it includes the activity workload information which must be accurately and consistently recorded for costs to be determined. (NB: Remember that 'costs' to be set against budgets consist of the volume of workload units completed, multiplied by the actual or standard 'unit cost' of a unit of workload.)

**6.4** The Körner programme has had wide-ranging objectives of improving the education and training of NHS staff in the more accurate and efficient collection of data, and in the managerial use of the resultant information, as well as in encouraging the greater use of computers and information technology throughout the Service. Nevertheless, arguably the most distinctive feature of the programme of the Steering Group has been its work on establishing standardized 'minimum data sets' (MDS) for each category of activity, manpower and financial information. For each category the MDS were basically to comprise those items of data which district level management needs in order to conduct efficient and effective management (within the constraints of data availability and cost).

If data is not useful to local management, then there is much concern that it may not be collected accurately and comprehensively. Therefore one role of the Steering Group has been to try to ensure that data is not demanded by regions and the DHSS for routine reporting to them, unless it is also useful to

District (or unit) management. A further role has been to emphasize the importance of linkage between different kinds of data, and the importance of these being collected and analysed on a compatible basis. For example, units of activity must be measured in terms which are feasible to cost, and reports on activity, manpower and finance should be standardized on identical dates to compare like with like.

*Körner recommendations on financial information*

**6.5**   Space here does not permit detailed listing, let alone discussion, of all the Körner Steering Group's recommendations on financial information in their Final Report, but we will attempt a summary. The Körner Group recommend continuation of the uniform subjective analysis of expenditure (their paragraph 2.8), with minor amendments as shown in the MDS in their Annex II. On budgetary procedures and analysis, Körner concluded that to prescribe a MDS for budgetary reports militates against necessary local flexibility (their paragraphs 2.9 to 2.11). Instead it commended a 'Code of Practice for Budgetary Control' which includes budgetary delegation as far down the management structure as practicable and otherwise makes many of the same points of good budgetary practice as we have already considered in Chapter 4. No advice was offered on whether or not clinicians should be brought into financial planning and accountability as budget holders, and it is understood that this was a conscious decision because there were varying opinions on clinical budgeting within the finance group.

**6.6**   The Körner Group made specific recommendations for MDS for both hospital and community services in respect of 'location analysis' (i.e. cost identification by 'site', compulsory for hospitals only) and 'departmental analysis' (their Annexes III to V). The important point is made that for each department work-units should be developed associated with the output of that particular department: this is an essential pre-condition for accurate, realistic allocation of costs to the specialties which generate the workload (i.e. services for patients) upon service departments (e.g. pathology, radiology).

**6.7**   The Körner Report went into some detail on the need for information on the costs of different services, and in particular the services delivered to different groups of patients. Their paragraph 2.23 states: 'We believe that the absence of a uniform, generally available cost analysis of different kinds of patient care in hospital and community services by patient group characteristics (e.g. age, diagnosis, specialty) severely limits the ability of districts to manage, and adversely affects planning, monitoring and performance evaluation at all levels.' The Report (paragraphs 2.24 to 2.29) then briefly lists and assesses the potential methods of producing cost information for patient care analysis: patient costing, diagnostic group costing, clinical team costing (i.e. costs traceable to a particular clinician, firm or clinical team), specialty costing, and client group costing (e.g. costing for the care of all children, the elderly, or mentally handicapped patients in a site or district). It concluded:

**a**   that patient costing would allow maximum flexibility in that such information may be aggregated by any characteristic or combination of characteristics held on patients' records; but also

b    that the development of patient costing has not yet reached a stage where the benefits derived can be assessed against the expense of implimentation.

We consider patient costing further in Chapter 9, together with diagnosis group costing.

## Körner recommendations on specialty costing

**6.8**    The Report pointed out (paragraph 2.25) that costing by client group uses categories which are not exclusive (e.g. the care of children and of the elderly spreads across specialty, locational and unit boundaries), and it implies that this may not be practical for information systems intended at least partly to improve cost control and efficiency (in this context also see 4.24 in Chapter 4 of this book). Additionally the Report points out that clinical team costing is a refinement of specialty costing. It then notes 'that specialty costing, achieved through direct allocation and opportionment of costs, has been field-tested in a variety of NHS situations and is of proven benefit'.

The Körner Report also concludes that while specialty costing may not take sufficient account of 'case mix' (in terms of condition, complexity and severity), it does take greater account of this than do the existing functional costing systems, so that the Report is therefore able to recommend that specialty costing be introduced as a routine reporting system in all health districts, for early implementation. Additionally, the Report encourages experimentation in patient costing or other systems more refined than specialty costing, provided that this does not detract from implementing specialty costing and other minimum core recommendations of the Report.

**6.9**    The Körner Report continues with technical advice of interest mainly to finance staff (paragraphs 2.30 to 2.33), but three points of more general interest may be extracted for comment. First (2.30c), the Report recommends that for inter-district and national comparisons, specialty costs should include all, and only, the expenditure on patient treatment services (i.e. Section A of their Annex III), although for other purpose (e.g. local performance review) districts may wish to include additional categories of expenditure as appropriate. The logic of this recommendation is not explained: common sense suggests that there will be at least as much variation between districts in the case mixes and treatment costs compared in what are nominally the same specialties, as in the indirect costs and overhead costs incurred outside of patient treatment services. A more sensible recommendation might have been *always* to report specialty costs in three parts: patient treatment costs + other costs = total specialty costs.

**6.10**    Secondly, the Report points out that specialty costing provides a transitional progression towards clinical costing and clinical budgeting, so that it is essential that districts moving towards these systems (discussed in Chapter 7) should implement specialty costing with constant regard to the next stage of development. The point for emphasis here is that the 'sampling' (or Magee) method of specialty costing discussed in the centre of this chapter is not adequate to support clinical budgeting, whereas the 'continuous' method of specialty costing discussed toward the end of the chapter is sufficient and indeed essential to the implementation of clinical or specialty budgeting.

**6.11**   Thirdly, the Report notes that the cost of implementing specialty costing will vary significantly between authorities. The costs of implementation will indeed vary widely according to:

a   the size and functional complexity of a district,
b   the accuracy and computerization already achieved in its activity and workload information systems, and
c   whether it is implementing the 'sampling' approach or the more sophisticated 'continuous' approach to specialty costing.

*Other Körner Report recommendations*

**6.12**   In paragraphs 2.47 to 2.51 of the Report the problems of accounting for the costs of equipment, vehicles and buildings are considered: we will return to these problems in Chapter 8. Most of the other main recommendations in the Report are of a technical nature, but amongst these it is worth mentioning that certain changes are suggested in the standardized financial reporting of districts to regions – which provides information for regions and the DHSS to assess compliance with district financial obligations, and to choose particular areas of expenditure for inquiry in performance reviews, in the light of comparative performance information obtained from all districts. In particular it is proposed that the separate annual accounts and cost returns currently submitted on different dates should be merged into one set of 'management accounts' submitted by the end of June each year. In addition there should be an annual specialty cost return for each district classified by broad patient groups (see paragraph 2.30d and Annex XIII of the Report). The latter recommendation links with the proposed introduction of specialty costing and reporting within districts. The extra cost of the annual specialty costing report should be largely offset by the savings on simplifying the merged annual accounts and cost returns. It has been of course a guiding objective of the Körner programme to improve the quality of management information without significantly increasing the costs of administration.

Readers seeking a wider review of the Körner Reports and their MDS and reporting prescriptions should consult *Introducing Körner* by Phil Windsor.

**6.13**   To conclude this section on the Körner Steering Group's work, two points may be stressed. First, the Financial Information Report should not be considered in isolation from the other Körner reports. Its contribution to advancing the state of NHS financial accountability and performance depends upon the effective adoption of the linked information developments proposed in the Körner report on manpower, and in the several reports on hospital, community and other activities and workload. Financial information *must* be linked with workload and output information.

The second point is that the Körner recommendations must be viewed in the context that the Steering Group was seeking to determine information improvements which it would be practicable and economical for *all* health districts to implement quickly, within three years in most cases (i.e. by April 1987 for most of the hospital information requirements, as per HC(84)10). Advanced systems of specialty costing, clinical budgeting and patient costing are not feasible for *universal* implementation within that times-scale – but of course this book is not limited by such a short time horizon and in later chapters we shall consider foreseeable financial information improvements which might become universally feasible within the next ten years or so.

**6.14** The remaining sections of this chapter will review in turn the three main approaches to specialty costing. These are the 'statistical' approach (not mentioned in Körner); the 'sampling' approach, more commonly known as the 'Magee system' and which formed the principal approach to specialty costing considered by the Körner Financial Information Working Group during the preparation of their interim report; and the 'continuous' approach which is being developed in the Körner financial information trial at Bromsgrove and Redditch Health Authority as well as in the latest CASPE projects and the demonstration projects for the introduction of Griffiths' clinical management budgets.

## Statistical specialty costing

**6.15** The statistical approach to specialty costing arose from the interest of health economists and econometricians to analyse the cost structure of health care (and especially acute hospital services) in more detail than was possible from the subjective and functional cost accounting systems in use for routine cost recording and reporting systems. In addition the DHSS desired to have specialty costs for planning studies, and after 1976 these were needed also for use in making cross-boundary flow adjustments to RAWP targets (i.e. the national funding targets determined by the formulae of the Resource Allocation Working Party), and subsequently for use in SIFT adjustments (i.e. adjustments for specialty case mix variation in teaching hospitals receiving target additions for the Service Increment for Teaching). Owing to the lack of suitable accounting information within the NHS, actual cost data classified by specialty was not available.

**6.16** The alternative to accounting data collected by specialty and analysed locally was to apply statistical regression techniques to data held centrally in the hospital cost returns, and in the SH3 returns for each hospital which show the numbers of available beds and occupied beds, and of inpatients, for some 40 clinical specialties. The statistical regression is a computerized averaging procedure used to determine which of the available items of data about resources and activity within specialties are related to the generation of expenditure, and then to determine the statistical average form of the relationship.

Given the hundreds of acute, mainly acute and partly acute hospitals included in the data input, with each hospital markedly different from every other in its specialty mix and cost characteristics, the statistical model acquires a high degree of predictive ability in determining the *national average* cost of individual specialties. And yet, however 'true' the national average cost generated by the statistical regression, it is by no means clear that such an overall average is necessarily a fair measure of the cost (or the target funding entitlement) of, for example, a specialty in a hospital providing a cross-boundary referral service as a regional or sub-regional specialty centre, or of the same specialty in a teaching hospital.

Aside from differences in case severity between different grades of hospital, there is the problem that the big specialties such as general medicine and general surgery may comprise a very different case mix (including expensive sub-specialties) in separate hospitals nominally of the same overall type or grade. And as case mix may vary greatly between firms and individual clinicians, national average specialty costs offer no help at that level in assessing performance or resource needs.

**6.17**  A national average specialty cost can provide useful information for large-scale planning, but note that this is the average *total* cost per case, not the average variable or marginal cost, so that the information is not helpful for planning small, marginal changes in the throughput of patient care. Another use for a national average specialty cost (whether derived from statistical analysis or (in future) from the mean or median average of universally reported average specialty costs notified by health districts) is to set up a 'marker' by which to assess or review performance. However, this will be possible only when the routine collection and reporting of specialty cost information discussed later in this chapter has been implemented.

*The NHS Financial Information Project on age/specialty analysis*

**6.18**  Like the Körner programme, the NHS Financial Information Project (FIP) based within the West Midlands Regional Health Authority was one of the DHSS supported developments encouraged by the RAWP and Royal Commission criticisms of the state of NHS financial and other management information. The main thrust of the FIP was to research the problems and uses of patient costing, and to develop systems for patient costing in both the hospital and community sectors.

The FIP's main work in these areas is appropriately covered in Chapter 9 of this book, but some aspects of their work also deserve attention in other chapters. In the FIP Overview Report it is emphasized that patient-based costing need not be seen as an 'all or nothing' system: it is an ultimate information system dependent upon many feeder systems of routine information each individually useful in planning and control.

Much of the work of the FIP was invested in developing or improving certain of the key feeder systems, e.g. activity/workload and costing information in hospital nursing, home nursing and theatres. Additionally the project team concluded that much greater use could be made of existing information through more rigorous analysis, including the use of computer modelling to assist district planning processes.

**6.19**  One FIP Report is on *Using Computer Models in Age/Specialty*

*Analysis.* This report could almost equally well be mentioned in Chapter 9, but we include it here because of its application in specialty cost analysis. The FIP developed a model on a microcomputer using the readily available 'spreadsheet' modelling package SUPERCALC. By apportioning expenditure attributed to functional headings in the hospital cost returns to specialties on the basis of cases, inpatient days or available bed days, it proved possible to approximate specialty costs. Using these specialty costs together with data on the number of patient days and cases in each age group/specialty from the HAA, a cost per case by age group and specialty was calculated and printed out for study. The model was then used to demonstrate how the true cost of the care of the elderly could be calculated, whereas existing systems can provide costs only for those of the elderly recorded as being under the care of the specialty of geriatrics.

The model has shown how costs per patient day vary by age group within individual specialties, and a further exercise with the model is to predict the effects on revenue expenditure of forecast changes in the future age structure of the population, analysed by age group and specialty. This is valuable planning information, even if the model does not separate out fixed and variable costs to allow the cost effects from small marginal changes in service provision to be predicted. And of course the specialty costs produced by the model are approximations only, and thus not sufficiently accurate (or, at least, provable) as to be useable in preparing and monitoring clinical budgets.

## Specialty costing based on sampling

### Background to specialty costing

**6.20** As explained in the preceding chapters, prior to 1974 the NHS's main costing system was for subjective costs (what inputs the money was spent on) for overall expenditure control. After 1974 the emphasis shifted to functional costs (which manager spent the money on what input) to link with the new functional management responsibility and budgetary control, and the 1982 reorganization mainly served to shift the emphasis within the functional approach from the district to the unit level. But almost since the inception of the NHS central planners, economists, clinicians and others have sought to have more sensitive costing information, linked to outputs (in the absence of information on outcomes) and classified by groups of patients. The clinicians' interests were typically strongest on detailed local information relevant to their own best use of resources as between different patient groups, and as between alternative patterns of therapy or patient mangement. This led naturally to concern for 'disease costing' or 'patient costing' which we consider in Chapter 9. The planners and economists' interests were stronger on larger aggregations of patients, with concern for marginal adjustments in the best use of resources between care groups, between specialties, between sites, and between hospital and community approaches to care. This converged with a growing awareness of the need for clinical and managerial sensitivity to costs.

**6.21** From the two latter, convergent interests arose support for the development of specialty costing. A fuller history and assessment of specialty costing is contained in Mr Ray Hillman's *Specialty Costing in the National Health Service*, to which the present author acknowledges a great debt for authoritative discussion on which he has drawn extensively. Mr Hillman's book is the definitive text on specialty costing, and it contains much detail on the working of specialty costing systems, and on their inter-linkages with the information requirements in the several Körner reports into which this present book does not have space to delve. That book includes information on patient costing and clinical budgeting develop-ments, and thus, like Jane Carter's *Recent Developments in Financial Infor-mation for Health Services*, it provides in part a parallel coverage to this present book, such as readers in search of greater technical detail or variety of opinion may wish to consult. The first major development was Magee specialty costing, an economical approach based on the sampling of workloads.

*Magee specialty costing*

**6.22** Following growing dissatisfaction with the quality of NHS cost infor-mation for planning, Professor Charles Magee of Cardiff (who had previous experience in costing cervical cytology screening) was commissioned by the DHSS to develop an inexpensive system of costing for specialties to provide useful information for planning. The development work was done at Bridgend Hospital with the assistance of Mr R.J. Osmolski and limited clerical resources. By the time of the Royal Commision's report substantial progress had been made, while somewhat similar developments had gone forward also at Harrogate, Southmead, North Tees and elsewhere. Accordingly there was sufficient progress and interest for the DHSS to fund trials of the 'Magee' specialty costing system in seven health districts. Before the end of these trials the interest had spread further, and one region (North East Thames) had committed itself to the introduction of specialty costing into all its Districts.

**6.23** The seven trial centres (one of these with two hospitals participating) are identified in the column headings of Table 6.1, reproduced from the Magee trial reports to illustrate one type of information produced from specialty costing. The trials were funded by a two-year DHSS grant of £9,000 per annum each, and the grants could be spent either on extra staff support or on extra computing. The trials were conducted using Professor Magee's *Manual for the Introduction of Specialty Costing*, with a steering committee of treasurers and DHSS representatives. There were frequent meetings between the research staff of the seven districts to try to ensure that the specialty costing developments proceeded on closely similar lines, so that the cost information from the trials would be as directly comparable as possible. The exact amount of time given to the trials by the existing staff of the seven districts has not been quantified and costed, but overall it is clear that the Magee form of specialty costing proved capable of introduction at modest overall cost.

**6.24** At the end of the trials a report and revised manual, by R.I. Hillman and G.R. Nix, was published by the DHSS, and this is now accessible as Appendix 1 in the previously mentioned book by Mr Hillman. The revised manual indicates that during the trials it was confirmed that while the Magee principles could be followed, it was necessary to vary the detailed methods of data collection or cost treatment when dealing with individual departments in the several districts. This was required by differences in organizational relationships, differences in data availability and differences in the level of computerization achieved between health districts at the time of the trials. Some of these differences might have been eliminated if substantially greater funding and/or time had been available in the trials. Realistically, in this author's view, it should be accepted as a fact of life for the predictable future that all new financial information systems will produce cost and budgetary information which is not completely comparable between different health districts. This will continue to be the case so long as health districts enjoy the autonomy of largely determining their own organizational structures, and their own methods and degrees of computerization and of data collection systems, and also so long as there continue to be significant variations in the case mix of nominally the same specialties between different health authorities.

**6.25** Attempts have been made to compare the results obtained from the statistical regression analysis of specialty costs with the results from the Magee trials. From one of these comparisons by Gwyn Bevan is reproduced Table 6.2. On the left of the table are DHSS national average specialty costs obtained from two separate runs of the regression model (for 1976–77 and for 1979–80), uplifted for inflation to 1980–81 price levels. On the right are the range of low and high costs for each specialty in the 1980–81 Magee trials reports (see Table 6.1), together with the 'true average' costs for the Magee sample. Even though the Magee sample is too small to yield dependable national average figures, the scale of difference between the Magee results and the DHSS results may give some cause for concern. Arguably, neither set of results necessarily represents the level of costs reasonably to be expected at any given hospital, given differences in the facilities provided, and the case mix treated.

**6.26** Magee specialty costing was designed to provide cost information of a sufficient accuracy for use in financial and operational planning, and in general performance reviews. But the accuracy is not nearly 100%, such as should be sought for any system of specialty costing used to report performance against specialty or clinical budgets where tight standards of budgetary performance are intended, and where issues of planned savings and virement may be crucial to motivation and acceptability (as we shall see in the next chapter). Probably the main reason for uncertainty over the level of accuracy achieved in Magee specialty costing arises from the fact that in the trial districts most of the supporting workload information systems (including notably radiology, pharmacy and pathology) were neither computerized nor organized to devote adequate clerical resources to the accurate classification and reporting of workload by specialty on a continuing basis. Accordingly recourse was made to sampling the workload to be costed, sometimes for periods as short as one week in a quarter.

*Table 6.1    Specialty costing 1980/81 – cost per case and length of stay*

| Specialty | District: Southmead<br>Hospital: Southmead | | Southmead<br>Ham Green | | Barking<br>Oldchurch | | Basingstoke<br>Basingstoke | |
|---|---|---|---|---|---|---|---|---|
| | £ | Days | £ | Days | £ | Days | £ | Days |
| General medicine | 662 | 10.0 | 880 | 15.6 | 476 | 10.4 | 692 | 12.6 |
| Paediatrics | 341 | 3.9 | — | — | 379 | 4.9 | 336 | 4.1 |
| Infectious diseases | — | — | 895 | 11.9 | — | — | — | — |
| Chest diseases | — | — | — | — | — | — | — | — |
| Dermatology | 3,016 | 52.5 | — | — | — | — | — | — |
| Neurology | — | — | — | — | 604 | 11.6 | — | — |
| Cardiology | — | — | — | — | — | — | — | — |
| Rehabilitation | — | — | — | — | — | — | — | — |
| Genito urinary medicine | — | — | — | — | — | — | — | — |
| Rheumatology | 1,277 | 15.3 | — | — | — | — | — | — |
| Geriatrics | 689 | 10.4 | 1,042 | 22.9 | 1,071 | 20.5 | 5,592 | 142.6 |
| Units for younger disabled | — | — | N/A | N/A | — | — | — | — |
| General surgery | 680 | 7.5 | 380 | 6.0 | 477 | 8.3 | 521 | 7.3 |
| ENT | 332 | 3.8 | — | — | 588 | 5.8 | 349 | 4.7 |
| Orthopaedic | 755 | 10.8 | — | — | 1,014 | 19.4 | 809 | 14.0 |
| Opthalmology | — | — | — | — | 507 | 9.9 | 475 | 5.7 |
| Radiotherapy | — | — | 834 | 12.6 | 855 | 14.5 | — | — |
| Urology | 654 | 7.8 | 448 | 5.9 | — | — | — | — |
| Plastic surgery | — | — | — | — | — | — | — | — |
| Thoracic surgery | — | — | — | — | — | — | 681 | 7.7 |
| Dental surgery | 367 | 2.8 | — | — | 347 | 3.3 | 267 | 2.6 |
| Orthodontics | — | — | — | — | — | — | — | — |
| Neurosurgery | — | — | — | — | 1,308 | 18.5 | — | — |
| Gynaecology | 318 | 3.7 | 293 | 4.0 | — | — | 425 | 5.9 |
| Obstetrics | 430 | 5.3 | — | — | — | — | | |
| Special care baby unit | 1,316 | 12.5 | — | — | — | — | — | — |
| Mental handicap | — | — | — | — | — | — | — | — |
| Mental illness | — | — | — | — | — | — | — | — |
| Nephrology | 467 | 4.9 | — | — | — | — | — | — |
| Renal transplant unit | 1,527 | 9.0 | — | — | — | — | — | — |
| Psycho-geriatric | — | — | 1,728 | 29.6 | — | — | — | — |
| GP – other | — | — | — | — | — | — | 2,322 | 43.3 |
| GP – maternity | — | — | — | — | — | — | 339 | 4.4 |
| Cardiac surgery | — | — | — | — | — | — | — | — |
| Haematology | — | — | — | — | — | — | — | — |
| Child psychiatry | — | — | — | — | — | — | — | — |
| Gastro-enterology | — | — | — | — | — | — | — | — |
| Accident & emergency | — | — | — | — | — | — | — | — |
| Other | — | — | — | — | — | — | — | — |
| Total/average | 539 | 6.6 | 696 | 11.9 | 570 | 10.1 | 571 | 9.4 |

Source: *DHSS Funded Research into Specialty Costing, 1980–1982*, by R.L. Hillman and G.R. Nix, Southmead Health Authority.

It is worth repeating that while the level of accuracy achieved in the Magee trials was almost certainly valuable for operational and strategic planning and performance review, it was not sufficient in that form to support specialty of clinical budgeting. Moreover, the degree of reliance on manual procedures and the limited amount of dedicated staff resources meant that the Magee specialty costs were not fully analysed and reported

*Table 6.1   Specialty costing 1980/81 – cost per case and length of stay*

| Specialty \ District Hospital | South Glamorgan UHW | | North Tees North Tees | | Manchester South Wythenshawe | | Harrogate Harrogate | |
|---|---|---|---|---|---|---|---|---|
| | £ | Days | £ | Days | £ | Days | £ | Days |
| General medicine | 645 | 9.6 | 401 | 7.7 | 583 | 9.9 | 467 | 7.3 |
| Paediatrics | 440 | 5.1 | 225 | 3.2 | 389 | 4.5 | — | — |
| Infectious diseases | — | — | — | — | — | — | — | — |
| Chest diseases | — | — | — | — | 671 | 12.3 | — | — |
| Dermatology | 1,028 | 18.9 | — | — | — | — | — | — |
| Neurology | 789 | 12.4 | — | — | — | — | — | — |
| Cardiology | 905 | 8.0 | — | — | 565 | 5.2 | — | — |
| Rehabilitation | — | — | — | — | — | — | — | — |
| Genito urinary medicine | — | — | — | — | — | — | — | — |
| Rheumatology | 1,060 | 15.4 | 682 | 14.2 | 1,227 | 27.8 | — | — |
| Geriatrics | 712 | 11.6 | 1,762 | 53.9 | 3,595 | 86.6 | — | — |
| Units for younger disabled | — | — | 3,400 | 94.6 | — | — | — | — |
| General surgery | 831 | 9.7 | 482 | 6.8 | 431 | 6.1 | 699 | 9.5 |
| ENT | 492 | 5.3 | — | — | 256 | 3.1 | 294 | 3.8 |
| Orthopaedic | 1,163 | 14.4 | 647 | 13.6 | 1,028 | 18.3 | 711 | 11.5 |
| Opthalmology | 565 | 5.8 | — | — | — | — | — | — |
| Radiotherapy | — | — | — | — | — | — | — | — |
| Urology | 511 | 6.4 | — | — | — | — | — | — |
| Plastic surgery | — | — | 504 | 4.0 | — | — | — | — |
| Thoracic surgery | — | — | — | — | 993 | 7.4 | — | — |
| Dental surgery | 411 | 3.5 | 274 | 2.5 | 240 | 1.6 | 314 | 2.7 |
| Orthodontics | — | — | — | — | — | — | — | — |
| Neurosurgery | 1,306 | 12.0 | — | — | — | — | — | — |
| Gynaecology | 349 | 4.8 | 283 | 4.6 | 267 | 3.6 | — | — |
| Obstetrics | 449 | 5.8 | 381 | 7.1 | 395 | 5.1 | — | — |
| Special care baby unit | 977 | 15.6 | 708 | 10.9 | 642 | 8.2 | — | — |
| Mental handicap | — | — | — | — | — | — | — | — |
| Mental illness | 1,692 | 29.9 | 2,301 | 63.4 | — | — | — | — |
| Nephrology | — | — | — | — | — | — | — | — |
| Renal transplant unit | — | — | — | — | — | — | — | — |
| Psycho-geriatric | — | — | — | — | — | — | — | — |
| GP – other | — | — | — | — | — | — | — | — |
| GP – maternity | — | — | 231 | 4.9 | — | — | — | — |
| Cardiac surgery | 2,708 | 13.9 | — | — | — | — | — | — |
| Haematology | 381 | 4.7 | — | — | — | — | — | — |
| Child psychiatry | — | — | 2,881 | 38.7 | — | — | — | — |
| Gastro-enterology | — | — | 525 | 10.7 | — | — | — | — |
| Accident & emergency | — | — | 94 | 1.7 | — | — | — | — |
| Other | — | — | 769 | 5.5 | — | — | — | — |
| Total/average | 668 | 8.3 | 555 | 11.9 | 626 | 8.9 | 346 | 4.7 |

until far longer after the end of each reporting period than would be acceptable in an ongoing system of budgetary control. In addition to the total costs per specialty illustrated in Table 6.1, specialty costs can be supplied showing the breakdown of functional, service and ward costs within the total for each separate specialty. The detail and accuracy of this will be the greater when specialty costing is used to report and monitor

Table 6.2   Comparison of costs per case by specialty

| Specialty | 1976–77 Reg. cost | Uplifted to 1980–81 ((1) × 1.828) | 1979–80 Reg. cost | Uplifted to 1980–81 ((3) × 1.2555) | Magee trials 1980–81 Range | Magee trials 1980–81 Number | Magee trials 1980–81 Average |
|---|---|---|---|---|---|---|---|
| | (1) | (2) | (3) | (4) | (5) | (6) | (7)[a] |
| General medicine | 348 | 636 | 485 | 609 | 401–880 | 8 | 573 |
| Paediatrics | 176 | 322 | 240 | 301 | 225–440 | 6 | 370 |
| Infectious diseases | 331 | 605 | 448 | 562 | | 1 | 895 |
| Chest diseases | 465 | 850 | 602 | 756 | | 1 | 671 |
| Dermatology | 505 | 923 | 730 | 916 | 1,028–3,016 | 2 | 1,074 |
| Neurology | 661 | 1,208 | 1,058 | 1,328 | 604–789 | 2 | 704 |
| Cardiology | 594 | 1,086 | 953 | 1,196 | 565–905 | 2 | 710 |
| Rehabilitation | 430 | 786 | 700 | 879 | | 0 | |
| Genito-urinary medicine | 339 | 620 | 443 | 556 | | 0 | |
| Rheumatology | 496 | 907 | 739 | 928 | 682–1,277 | 4 | 873 |
| Geriatrics | 967 | 1,768 | 1,610 | 2,021 | 712–3,595 | 7 | 1,735 |
| YDU | 2,632 | 4,811 | 2,707 | 3,399 | | 1 | 3,400 |
| General surgery | 232 | 424 | 359 | 451 | 380–831 | 8 | 576 |
| ENT | 163 | 298 | 264 | 331 | 256–588 | 6 | 373 |
| Orthopaedic | 407 | 744 | 597 | 749 | 647–1,163 | 7 | 848 |
| Ophthalmology | 215 | 393 | 352 | 442 | 475–565 | 3 | 528 |
| Radiotherapy | 387 | 707 | 539 | 677 | 834–855 | 2 | 845 |
| Urology | 323 | 590 | 462 | 580 | 448–654 | 3 | 541 |
| Plastic surgery | 348 | 636 | 492 | 618 | | 1 | 504 |
| Thoracic surgery | 631 | 1,153 | 1,016 | 1,275 | 681–993 | 2 | 837 |
| Dental surgery | 133 | 243 | 229 | 287 | 240–411 | 7 | 323 |
| Orthodontics | 156 | 285 | 334 | 419 | | 0 | |
| Neurosurgery | 659 | 1,205 | 1,063 | 1,334 | 1,306–1,308 | 2 | 1,307 |
| Gynaecology | 179 | 327 | 241 | 302 | 267–425 | 6 | 302 |
| Obstetrics | 201 | 367 | 270 | 339 | 381–449 | 5 | 418 |
| SCBU | 218 | 398 | 322 | 404 | 642–1,316 | 4 | 941 |
| GP maternity | 166 | 303 | 235 | 295 | 231–339 | 2 | 295 |
| GP other | 285 | 521 | 450 | 565 | | 1 | 2,322 |
| Other specialist units | 280 | 512 | 452 | 567 | 94–2,880 | 7 | 430 |

[a]These are true averages (i.e. total costs of Magee trial hospitals divided by total inpatient days). The figure for other specialist units (OSU) includes any Magee specialty costs that would be classified under OSU and the SH3 hospital return.

Sources: Magee costs: G. R. Nix, Southmead District; Regression costs: Price Index; SH3 statistics: DHSS and Welsh Office.

expenditure against specialty or clinical budgets, and this will be discussed and illustrated in Chapter 7.

*Specialty costing by sampling*

**6.27**   Henceforth Magee specialty costing will be referred to as 'specialty costing by sampling'. This is out of no disrespect for Professor Magee, whose essential principles will continue into future systems of specialty costing, but simply to give emphasis to the fact that the pioneering Magee specialty costing was a low cost system designed when local computing capacity for 'feeder systems' (i.e. supporting data systems) was still in very short supply in the NHS, and when expectations did not extend so far as to provide feeder workload and specialty costing systems capable of supporting specialty or clinical budgeting as well. Nevertheless, Magee specialty costing by sampling was a success relative to its objectives, and the Körner Interim Report noted the benefits: better information for planning, useful information for functional budget holders regarding their service provision to clinicians, improved accuracy of expenditure information as between inpatient and outpatient services, and generally more useful information for resource use evaluation and performance review.

**6.28**   The Körner Interim Report on financial information was published in July 1983 when the quality of information available from the Magee trials probably seemed adequate. The Körner Final Report on Financial Information was completed in July 1984. In the intervening year the Griffiths Management Inquiry had reported, and the demonstrations of clinical management budgeting (see Chapter 7) had begun. Expectations had risen. Thus, while the Körner Final Report includes some references to specialty costing little changed from the Interim Report (including the references in paragraph 2.33 to the low cost of implementing (Magee-style) specialty costing), its main prescriptive statement on specialty costing sets more stringent requirements, as follows:

> 2.31   The information required to produce specialty costs . . . is compatible with, and can provide transition to, clinical costing and clinical budgeting. For both these more detailed information . . . is required. . . . It is essential that districts moving towards clinical costs and budgets should implement specialty costing with constant regard to the next stage of development.

*Other developments in costing specialties*

**6.29**   There have been other developments of information systems designed to cost specialties and having to rely on sampling or otherwise incomplete information. Some, by clinicians, have produced specialty cost information as a by-product of patient or disease costing information. Typically such clinically led developments have been planned to provide information for the use only of clinicians (sometimes because the system held confidential patient data), for review of patient management or to provide data for medical audit. Other developments have been initiated by finance staff, or by researchers. We will mention just two such developments.

The first, the CASPE programme at the King's Fund, has specialty costing as very much a secondary aspect relative to the greater involvement of clinicians in planning and financial decisions, and detailed discussion of this will be more appropriate in the next chapter. The second, the SCS (specialty costing system) at St Thomas' Hospital, London, is well decumented by Jane Carter. This was a pioneering project which was linked with extensive computer systems developments. It provided useful information for internal district planning, and for use in resource allocation debates with the regional health authority. It has been superseded by a newer system, adaptable to closer analysis of fixed and variable costs within specialties, and capable of supporting clinical management budgets. This is consistent with the quoted Körner Report finding of the need to have regard for the next stage of development, which may be represented by 'continuous specialty costing'.

## Continuous specialty/clinical costing

**6.30** 'Continuous' specialty costing is simply an evolutionary development from Magee specialty costing based on sampling. The principles are the same. The differences are that workload data is continuously collected and recorded, rather than sampled, so that it can be highly accurate, and that owing to the continuous collection and processing of data, progress reports are quickly available and regularly supplied. To achieve these differences requires planning, motivation and good discipline in data collection, as well as extensive computerization in recording all main activity and workload data sets.

This approach is very similar to the industrial model of costing. It requires very substantial inputs of systems design and of data checking and processing in the early stages, as well as investment in further computerization. Thus it increases management costs in the short term, although in the longer term when all major information sets are computerized and staff are fully trained it may be possible that the recurrent revenue costs of improved cost information systems will be little greater than today's costs. Moreover, the development of accurate specialty costing systems should repay itself many times over through the improvement obtained in cost, activity and manpower information for better planning and control, especially if clinical budgeting is also adopted (see Chapter 7).

**6.31** Specialty costing may be subdivided further by accurate coding to cost the work of firms within specialties or to cost the work of individual consultants as may be needed for Griffiths clinical management budgets. Of course, the smaller the organizational component of clinical work which is costed, the more demanding become the activity and workload measurement and record-keeping requirements. Often the beds of an entire ward are allocated to one specialty, so that all resources or services supplied to that ward or to its patients as individuals may be recorded unequivocally as a charge to that specialty. In contrast, a firm, or certainly an individual clinician, will normally use only a part of one or more wards, using beds which may vary somewhat in number and location from day to day. In such cases there must be much more detailed attention given to identifying the exact consultant responsible for each patient, bed, test, etc., if accurate costs for these are to be correctly recorded, coded and charged.

### Costing for managerial responsibility

**6.32**  Under the functional budgeting system, even as amended for the new unit structures, the allocation of budgets and the consequential cost reporting of budget expenditure to demonstrate accountable performance, does not always mirror true managerial responsibility. Let us illustrate this from the real-life example of a radiology department.

The basic problem was that the pay of those staff working in the department but professionally answerable to someone outside the department was not included in the departmental budget or cost accounts. Clerks, receptionist and secretaries in this radiology department were on the budget and cost report of the patient services officer. Attending nursing staff were on the nursing budget, portering staff on an administrator's budget and medical staff on the budget of the RHA. The maintenance engineers attached to the department were on the works department budget.

From the point of view of (departmental) managerial control and responsibility the situation just described seems ridiculous. And from the viewpoint of reporting correctly the full costs of radiology to be divided among all user specialties or individual clinicians, the situation is well nigh intolerable. The risk of error from overlooking important component costs, or from failing to reallocate them correctly from so many different budget headings, is too great. The new post-Körner *NHS Manual for Accounts* should help to resolve this problem of cost allocation.

**6.33**  Figure 6.1 attemps to illustrate in a simplified model what has to be done to obtain correct cost classifications in the charging or recharging of costs to specialties (or to individual clinicians). The illustration shows four different types of levels of cost centre, around each of which budgets, performance indicators and reviews can be constructed. The top level shows the total cost expenditure of a unit, divided into the functional management

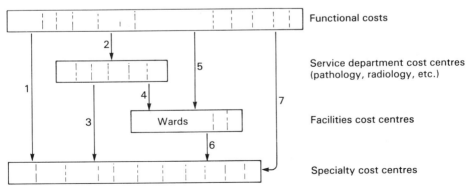

*Fig. 6.1   Flow of relevant costs within hospital management units.*

cost/budget centres with which we have been familiar since 1974. At the bottom level we have the total of costs charged, allocated or apportioned (see Glossary) to the specialties within the unit.

It is the two intermediate levels in the illustration which may be conceptually new to readers. However, they are essential for meaningful cost measurement and control, and they are required for the effective working of the clinical budgeting discussed in the next chapter. The second level in the illustration is labelled to show service department cost centres such as radiology, physiotherapy or pharmacy. The third level is labelled 'facilities', a term designating wards, operating theatres, outpatient clinics or other organizational entities in which patient treatment takes place. Nurses are usually managerially responsible for facilities cost (and budget) centres.

**6.34**    Figure 6.1 displays several numbers alongside arrows. The arrows indicate flows of accountability and the charging of costs from one level to another, and the numbers key the particular flows to explanations in the numbered sub-paragraphs below:

1    The first arrow represents those functional expenditures which are directly chargeable to specialty or clinical cost centres. Medical salaries and overtime (UMTs), medical equipment and certain consumables are obvious examples. Medical secretaries and perhaps some other clinically determined resource costs should probably also be included here.
2    The second arrow represents functional expenditures charged for the resource requirements of the service departments. The example in 6.32 illustrates the range of functional costs which need to be brought together in one service cost centre, radiology. It is arguable that the service department's share of administrative costs and of some estates costs (e.g. heating costs, or the maintenance cost of departmental premises) should be charged to its cost centre additionally.
3    The third arrow represents the recharging of service department costs for tests and other services ordered by clinicians to specialty or clinical cost centres. This requires accurate records of workload, including evidence on the cost of each unit of workload, or at least an equitable weighting system for approximating these costs. Note that the exact, actual cost at 3 can only be determined after the costs charging at 2 has been completed. To overcome the likely delay in this, as well as to separate responsibility for volume (variable costs) from responsibility for establishment (fixed costs), it is probably desirable that the recharge as 3 should be in two parts, a standard variable cost per unit and, separately, a standard fixed charge (see 3.15 to 3.18 in Chapter 3).
4    The fourth arrow indicates that, while many services are rendered direct to specialties, other services are rendered through the facilities, eventually to benefit the patients of specialties or individual clinicians as 'indirect costs'. A clear example is pharmacy, which supplies medication both directly to clinical prescription, and often indirectly to top up ward stocks held in the ward facility.
5    The fifth arrow represents the functional costs, dominated by nursing

pay, which enter into the total costs of facilities. But once again there is the question of how far administrative, estate and other back-up costs should be apportioned to the facilities cost centres before these in turn are recharged to specialty or clinical cost centres.

6     The sixth arrow is analogous to the third, representing recharge of facilities costs to clinical care. As noted earlier, if the recharging is to individual clinicians rather than to specialties or even firms, then the accuracy of record keeping and coding needed is much higher. Also there arises the question of how far different groups of patients need different levels of nursing care and impose significantly different costs. This involves the question of 'nursing dependency', a topic explored in some depth by the FIP and to which we will return later.

7     The seventh arrow represents the often substantial overheads of central administration, estates and other back-up services which will not have been charged out under the arrangements covered by arrows 1, 2 or 5. It is not obvious that overheads (e.g. grounds maintenance or payments in lieu of rates) which are remote from clinical management responsibility should be charged to specialty or clinical cost centres. To do so indeed violates standard practice in management responsibility accounting in industrial organizations – even though all overheads must of course be charged in industry to the financial accounting records kept for determining the cost of sales and the value of unsold stocks, for which the NHS has no direct accounting equivalent! The Körner Final Report recommends in paragraph 2.30c that 'for inter-district and national comparisons, specialty costs should include all and only the expenditure in Section A (patient treatment services) of the departmental analysis in Annex III, although for other purposes districts may wish to include additional expenditure as appropriate'. This is in contrast to the advice from the Griffiths Management Inquiry Report of 1983 which recommends that all the overheads of each health authority should be redistributed among the clinical management cost centres, apparently so that the scale of overheads relative to patient-care costs can be clearly seen, and pressure can be generated to cut overhead costs.

**6.35**   Let us conclude this chapter with an example of one form of information report which might become universally available from 1988 as a consequence of the collection and processing of data from April 1987 (for hospital services) to meet Körner requirements. Table 6.3 is an extract from the Körner specialty cost returns for Bradford Health District, Bradford being one of four health districts providing field trials for the development of Körner financial information and the revision of the *NHS Manual for Accounts*. Space does not permit reproducing the entirety of the specialty cost returns, which themselves are only a small portion of the total Körner expenditure and cost analysis which may run to some sixty pages or more. But Table 6.3 does capture the required subdivisions of expenditure allocated and apportioned between major acute specialties.

Even so, readers may be bemused as to what useful information or guidelines for action can be derived by studying Table 6.3. Fair comment, as such information may only become really useful when it can be subjected to comparative performance review. This will involve access to and active

*Table 6.3  Specialty cost returns*

| Patient group | Code | | Patients using a bed (including day cases) | | | Outpatients | | | Day care patients | | |
|---|---|---|---|---|---|---|---|---|---|---|---|
| | Main | Sub | Expenditure 35 | Patient days 36 | Consultant episodes 37 | Expenditure 38 | Total attendances 39 | Referrals 40 | Expenditure 41 | Total attendances 42 | First attendances 43 |
| **Specialties** | | | | | | | | | | | |
| A. MEDICAL SPECIALTIES | | | | | | | | | | | |
| (a) Paediatrics | 101 | | 1,101,068 | 16,946 | 3,658 | 104,213 | 12,047 | 1,571 | | | |
| (b) Geriatrics | 102 | | 5,248,490 | 157,935 | 2,933 | 77,479 | 9,005 | 499 | 5,600 | 13,832 | 387 |
| (c) Other medical | 125 | | 4,996,575 | 111,384 | 3,898 | 317,596 | 81,907 | 16,507 | | | |
| SUB TOTAL A | 199 | | 11,346,133 | 286,265 | 10,489 | 499,287 | 102,959 | 18,577 | 5,600 | 13,832 | 387 |
| B. SURGICAL SPECIALTIES | | | | | | | | | | | |
| (a) General surgery & urology | 201 | | 4,805,876 | 63,685 | 10,584 | 499,982 | 25,266 | 8,402 | | | |
| (b) Orthopaedics | 202 | | 3,142,248 | 50,779 | 7,037 | 125,575 | 52,753 | 15,781 | | | |
| (c) ENT | 203 | | 992,390 | 12,543 | 4,748 | 26,906 | 21,271 | 6,783 | | | |
| (d) Ophthalmology | 204 | | 650,954 | 7,021 | 2,083 | 67,716 | 20,043 | 4,017 | | | |
| (e) Gynaecology | 205 | | 1,168,768 | 18,291 | 4,933 | 23,759 | 12,343 | 4,027 | | | |
| (f) Dental specialties | 206 | | 113,043 | 1,228 | 897 | 212,321 | 10,507 | 2,472 | | | |
| (g) Neurosurgery | 207 | | 52,824 | | | 118,502 | 353 | 147 | | | |
| (h) Plastic surgery | 208 | | 674,638 | 9,608 | 2,141 | 52,663 | 8,741 | 1,802 | | | |
| (i) Other surgical | 225 | | 568,046 | 4,684 | 1,225 | 35,548 | 1,738 | 1,802 | | | |
| SUB TOTAL B | 299 | | 12,168,786 | 167,839 | 33,648 | 1,162,971 | 153,015 | 45,233 | | | |

| | | | | | | | | | | |
|---|---|--:|--:|--:|--:|--:|--:|--:|--:|--:|
| **C. MATERNITY FUNCTION** | | | | | | | | | | |
| (a) Obstetrics and gynaecology | 301 | 3,960,652 | 48,289 | 838 | 81,553 | 39,197 | 6,875 | | | |
| (b) General practice | 302 | 1,659 | 2,470 | | | | 6,875 | | | |
| SUB TOTAL C | 399 | 3,962,311 | 50,759 | 838 | 81,553 | 39,197 | 13,750 | | | |
| **D. PSYCHIATRIC SPECIALTIES** | | | | | | | | | | |
| (a) Mental handicap | 401 | 2,770,883 | 158,521 | 446 | 2,699 | 293 | 300 | | | |
| (b) Other psychiatric | 405 | 1,267,614 | 74,718 | 1,112 | 121,363 | 8,530 | 856 | 52,937 | 14,174 | 162 |
| SUB TOTAL D | 499 | 4,038,497 | 233,239 | 1,558 | 124,062 | 8,823 | 1,156 | 52,937 | 14,174 | 162 |
| TOTAL CARRIED FORWARD | | 31,515,727 | 738,102 | 46,533 | 1,867,873 | 303,994 | 78,716 | 58,537 | 28,006 | 549 |

Source: Bradford Health Authority, *Körner Accounts, 1985/86*, p. 53.

comparison with similar data from 'similar' districts, or regional or national averages. Or, after a few years of running the system locally, useful insights may be derived from 'trend analysis' – that is plotting and studying the *relative* performance of different specialties through time. To assist in this, we need supplementary information on averages of cost per case, per day and per attendance/episode, and of LOS.

**6.36** But even so the information from specialty cost returns will not be first-class for managerial and clinical information needs. First, specialty costing shows only historical performance, after the event, and without linking this to pre-planned targets, i.e. budgets, of what can and should be achieved. Secondly, it does not subdivide cost or expenditure between individual consultants, thus diluting accountability and the usefulness of the information for consultants interested in studying their own use of resources. These aspects will now be considered in Chapters 7 and 8. Thirdly, the method is not able to take account of the variations in case mix between different hospitals (and individual consultants), which variances could explain and even justify differences in relative levels of expenditure (see Chapter 9).

## Conclusions

**6.37** The main points to emerge from this chapter are as follows:

a   that specialty costs determined by regression analysis are sufficiently accurate to be useful for planning and possibly for performance reviews, but they have no use in specialty or clinical budgeting, while their accuracy for use in cross-boundary flow adjustments and SIFT adjustments has been challenged on grounds of equity;
b   that specialty costs based on sampling of workload in service departments are useful for planning, but will not be sufficiently accurate and credible for monitoring specialty or clinical budgeting; and
c   that the continuous recording and costing of workload in all major departments is essential for achieving tight cost control and for reporting costs chargeable to specialty or clinical budgets.

Continous specialty costing is now being developed in a number of health districts, notably those involved in Griffiths, CASPE and MIPP clinical costing and budgeting trials and demonstrations.

## Summary

1 For years there has been interest in costing clinical work. Clinicians and other researchers attempted this on a short-term research basis. The researches were difficult because of lack of accurate records of workload (by specialty or clinician) in many diagnostic, para-medical and other service departments, and also lack of complete and reliable unit costs for the outputs of these departments.

2 The DHSS needed average treatment costs per specialty for use in cross-boundary flow adjustments to regional funding, for SIFT, and for analysis. Given the absence of real-life specialty costs, the DHSS developed a computerized information model, using statistical regression analysis, to derive approximate average specialty costs.

3 About ten years ago Professor C.C. Magee developed a simple and inexpensive system for routine, regular measurement and reporting of specialty costs in acute hospitals. This was later piloted in eight hospitals with encouraging results, thought useful for planning. However, inadequacies in workload recording (by accountable specialty) and in unit costs of departments meant that there was a margin of error or approximation in Magee specialty costs which made them unsuitable as a base on which to build specialty budgets for control.

4 The Körner programme from 1980 worked to improve activity and workload data and reporting, and also to improve the quality of costs charged to departments and which could form the basis for more accurate unit costs. On this prospect of improved 'feeder' data, the Körner Sixth Report was able to recommend the universal adoption of specialty costing for districts, commencing from 1987–88. The Report added, in effect, that if districts were planning to go beyond basic specialty costing to more sophisticated systems (e.g. specialty or clinical budgeting, patient or case mix costing, etc.) then extra effort would have to be put into improving workload and departmental unit costs to a higher standard. In other words, the 'feeder systems' would have to be more accurate, continuously up to date, more computerized, and capable of yielding accurate performance and cost figures promptly after the end of each month.

5 Accurate coding of accountability to the individual specialty or clinician for every item of service rendered by supporting patient treatment services is of the essence in making specialty costing an effective information system. Similarly, all relevant functional costs must be traced and reallocated to treatment services departments, so that clinicians can know the full amount of the unit costs of each type and item of tests and other services they request, the costs of which add up to comprise the main input costs of their own specialty.

# CHAPTER 7
# Clinical management budgets

**7.1** Clinical management budgets acquired 'headline status' in health services periodicals following their strong endorsement in the Griffiths Inquiry Report. Many readers will have viewed clinical management budgets (CMBs) as a 'flavour of the month', and some may hope to see CMBs fade away to oblivion. The first perception is doubtless realistic, but the latter hope is probably neither realistic nor, in the author's opinion, desirable. Clinical management budgets simply comprise the disaggregation of NHS unit budgets to the level of clinicians as budget holders for the costs incurred by their clinical work. We shall use the term to cover budgets for specialties, for firms within specialties, or for individual clinicians: in the longer run it may be assumed that CMBs will customarily relate to individual clinicians, as when good quality information is available it would seem only logical in human nature that individual clinicians will prefer to hold budgets directly related to their own work, rather than to the work of some larger group.

Table 7.1 illustrates what a monthly progress report for a CMB looks like. The obvious difference from a specialty costing report is the inclusion of 'budget' figures for the current month, and year to date. This allows actual cost within the specialty to be compared to budget, the difference between these being printed out by the computer in the 'Variance' column. Minus signs in the variance column indicate savings or improvements on budget targets.

The report reproduced is a real-life example from Southmead District, which has been involved in both the Magee trials and the Griffiths demonstrations. The report shows key activity indicators additional to budgetary expenditure. It is a summary report: more detailed supplementary reports could be made available on key areas, e.g. Ward Costs. It will be noted that the budget headings include only patient treatment costs: this conforms to Körner and the views of most treasurers, but it stops short of the original Griffiths recommendations which indicated that general support costs and overheads should be allocated or apportioned to all CMBs.

Table 7.1 serves also to illustrate a common management problem in UK specialties. During the period covered the specialty has increased admissions beyond budget by higher bed utilization (and without reducing LOS). As a result the 'efficiency indicators' of average cost per case and average cost per patient day show improvement, through spreading fixed costs over a larger workload. But of course variable or consumable costs have had to increase to cope with the extra volume of care provided, so that overall the specialty has overspent its budget for the three month period covered.

**7.2** Clinical management budgeting is currently the 'state of the art frontier' in NHS financial information systems and their managerial application. It would therefore be tempting for this chapter to expand into a technical manual of methodology, or into a 'buyer's guide' assessing the relative merits of the competing approaches. Leaving aside the author's limited qualifications for either of these approaches, the documentation available from the eight main trials recently involved in clinical management budgeting amounts to a stack nearly a foot high (and presumably equalling at least twice the word length of *War and Peace*!) so that no single chapter could cope with a full technical assessment.

The problem is that effective CMBs bring together at one point of focus all the developments in improved information detail and accuracy which have been evolving previously under the separate programmes in Körner information, specialty costing and information computerization for the NHS. Four of the eight trials are linked to the Griffiths Management Inquiry, three are linked to the CASPE (Clinical Accountability, Service Planning and Evaluation) programme based at the King's Fund, and the eighth, MIPP, is linked to the DHSS and derives from the Körner Steering Group on Health Services Information.

Without going so far as to suggest a 'best buy' among the three approaches, we shall consider their distinctive features in the context of explaining the general framework and operational characteristics of clinical budgeting later in this chapter. Our overall view is that there is much to be learned from all three approaches, and that eventually they will become melded into a single model of good practice. However, before going into the detail of the operational framework and the three approaches, we must first explain the background, objectives and principles of clinical management budgeting (CMB), also termed simply 'clinical budgeting'.

**7.3** The principles discussed in this chapter apply broadly to the whole of the NHS. But the detailed discussion of budget systems etc. will relate only to the acute/hospital sector. The quality of the available information for planning and control in the acute/hospital sector may be weak, but it is weaker still and in need of greater development in the community health sector. This is illustrated by the fact that the new Körner minimum data sets and other revised information requirements came into effect from April 1987 for the acute/hospital sector, but only from April 1988 for the community health sector. And some would say that compliance by April 1988 in the community health sector is setting a very optimistic target. Funds have been scant for research and development of the management information needs and systems for community health. The two main initiatives in this area have been from the Financial Information Project and from the Körner programme, and we report on these, and their implications for costing and budgeting in the community health services, in a later section.

*Table 7.1    Monthly progress report for a clinical management budget*

| [ Budget | Current month Actual | Variance ] | Expenditure head |
|---|---|---|---|
| 3,460 | 3,360 | – 100 | Consultants |
| 1,130 | 261 | – 869 | Senior registrars |
| | | | Registrars |
| 2,409 | 2,336 | – 73 | Senior house officers |
| 1,296 | 1,202 | – 94 | House officers |
| | | | House officers (locums) |
| | 554 | 554 | Medical non–NHS |
| 1,004 | 990 | – 14 | Secretaries |
| 21 | 73 | 52 | Patient's appliances |
| 42,695 | 49,914 | 7,219 | Ward costs |
| 17,018 | 21,770 | 4,752 | Theatre costs |
| 1,580 | 2,219 | 639 | Radiology |
| 7,325 | 7,480 | 155 | Pathology |
| 454 | 637 | 183 | ECG/medical photography |
| 642 | 668 | 26 | Paramedical services |
| 79,034 | 91,464 | 12,430 | |
| 451.62 | 473.91 | 22.29 | Cost per case £ |
| 91.16 | 86.12 | – 5.04 | Cost per patient day £ |
| | | | Activity analysis |
| 135 | 143 | 8 | Patients discharged |
| 40 | 50 | 10 | Day cases |
| | | | Bed usage |
| 867 | 1,062 | 195 | Occupied bed days |
| 6.4 | 7.4 | 1.0 | Average length of stay |
| | | | Theatre usage |
| 117 | 123 | 6 | Session hours made available |
| 91 | 100 | 9 | Inpatient hours |
| 23 | 24 | 1 | Day case hours |
| 114 | 124 | 10 | List hours used |
| 97.44 | 100.81 | 3.37 | % Utilization |
| 8 | 8 | | Emergency hours |
| – 3 | – 3 | | Transferred hours |
| 119 | 129 | 10 | Hours charged |
| 143.01 | 168.76 | 25.75 | Cost per theatre hour £ |

Source: Southmead Health Authority.

## Background to clinical management budgets

### What is CMB?

**7.4**    There is nothing new in the idea of consultants, whether individually or as members of firms or specialties, holding budgets for the costs of resources consumed in serving their patients. And consultants in radiology and pathology have long experience of budget holding. What is new is to have (a) government strongly endorsing – although not imposing – the

| [ Budget | Year to date Actual | Variance ] | Annual budget | Budget changes |
|---|---|---|---|---|
| 10,380 | 10,079 | – 301 | 41,544 | 11,224 |
| 3,390 | 2,449 | – 941 | 13,576 | |
| | | | | |
| 7,227 | 7,183 | – 44 | 28,922 | |
| 3,888 | 3,622 | – 266 | 15,578 | |
| | | | | |
| | 642 | 642 | | |
| 3,012 | 3,002 | – 10 | 12,073 | |
| 63 | 114 | 51 | 260 | |
| 128,613 | 136,882 | 8,269 | 515,190 | |
| 50,599 | 56,496 | 5,897 | 209,159 | |
| 4,792 | 5,429 | 637 | 19,291 | 12 |
| 22,219 | 21,527 | – 692 | 89,325 | 164 |
| 1,378 | 1,068 | – 310 | 5,585 | |
| 1,948 | 2,283 | 335 | 7,913 | |
| 237,509 | 250,776 | 13,267 | 958,416 | 11,400 |
| | | | | |
| 451.54 | 440.73 | – 10.81 | 448.91 | |
| 90.34 | 80.33 | – 10.01 | 90.25 | |
| | | | | |
| 406 | 432 | 26 | 1,640 | |
| 120 | 137 | 17 | 495 | |
| | | | | |
| 2,629 | 3,122 | 493 | 10,620 | |
| 6.5 | 7.2 | 0.7 | 6.5 | |
| | | | | |
| 349 | 349 | | 1,446 | |
| 270 | 303 | 33 | 1,142 | |
| 72 | 55 | – 17 | 304 | |
| 342 | 358 | 16 | 1,446 | |
| 97.99 | 102.58 | 4.59 | 100.00 | |
| 24 | 46 | 22 | 107 | |
| – 9 | – 17 | – 8 | – 47 | |
| 357 | 387 | 30 | 1,506 | |
| 141.73 | 145.98 | 4.25 | 138.88 | |

Source: Southmead Health Authority.

introduction of clinical budgets, (b) the medical professions accepting this innovation experimentally, and (c) the introduction of the word 'management' inserted between 'clinical' and 'budgets'. The important implication of this emphasis upon 'management' we shall explore further later in this chapter.

*History of clinical budgeting*

**7.5** Historically, most consultants have not wished to become involved in costs, budgets or financial control, except either occasionally in the context of research projects relating to their own work, or else through service on advisory committees examining wider financial problems of a hospital or district. This has been the typical experience in other countries also, although in a few cases, notably in the USA, some clinicians have in effect transferred from medicine to management and become financial controllers of hospital services.

In Britain, as in other countries, there has been concern that holding budgets might conflict with clinical autonomy and with the implicit obligation to obtain the best resources available for individual patients treated (we shall return to this problem later). There has also been concern that time spent in studying costs and budgets was a waste, a diversion from time properly spent in clinical activity. Relevant to this concern, it has been calculated in one of the districts currently piloting clinical management budgeting that there are more than fifty committees and working parties on which consultants serve, and which in greater or lesser degree include in their discussions matters of resource provision, budgets, costs, efficiency, etc. Thus it is arguable that if clinicians hold budgets within firmly determined unit allocations, then many of the committees and working parties which exist mainly to influence patterns of resource use would become redundant, and the time saved from these by consultants might at least equal the time they would need to give to managing their own clinical budgets.

**7.6**   The history of clinical budgeting in Britain has been documented best by Dr Iden Wickings (see Glossary under Clinical Budgeting). He was himself directly involved in what was possibly the first planned research and development project for clinical budgeting in the UK. This was at the Westminster Hospital in 1973–74 and has been fully reported: the overall conclusion was that if clinicians individually, or working together as a team with nurses, held budgets which included the right to deploy at least part of any savings achieved to alternative clinical uses, then some savings would be made, and also service improvements would be made which would not otherwise have occurred at that time, i.e. without the stimulus of involvement in the budgeting exercise. In later research at Brent Health District budgeting was not used, but instead there was the monthly provision to consultants of clinical costing and workload information. Summary reports were presented also to the cogwheel divisions and the DMT. Consultants were enabled to compare their own firm's performance with that of colleagues' firms.

Even after three years there was no evidence, comparing Brent's performance with that of other districts, to show that any consultants' pattern of work or expenditure had changed markedly (*BMJ* **286**). This led Dr Wickings to the general conclusion that cost information on its own has little impact upon clinical performance or demands upon resources.

This conclusion is broadly supported by other studies in the USA. There has been some contrary evidence, notably in assessing the response of nurses and ancillary workers to the placing of pricetags on consumables used in wards – but it may be that consultants tend to think in thousands of pounds, whereas nurses and ancillary staff tend to make price comparisons to their own domestic shopping lists!

7.7    The lack of involvement by clinicians in budgeting and financial control over the resources used in their own services has also been common in most of Europe. Even in the USA, where financial and activity information has been most heavily computerized and most closely analysed, this was not until recently done on the basis of the specialty or the individual clinician as the resource controller – if only for the reason that hospital income was generated on the basis of item-of-service cost-plus reimbursement against continually increasing demand for hospital care.

But the growth in demand for clinical care has slowed in the USA in the face of rising costs, and concern for the public purse has led to the change in US Federal Government funding of Medicare (for the elderly) from a cost-plus to a pre-determined case-cost basis. This has been made possible by the use of diagnosis related groups (DRGs) to analyse the costliness of clinical workload, and we will discuss this more fully in Chapter 9 in the context of developments to enable future NHS clinical activities to be costed and funded relative to the actual workloads experienced. This and other pressures have caused American hospitals to scrutinize their organizations and cost structures, and perhaps the best known example is the system of decentralized management and specialty unit financial control and budgeting at the Johns Hopkins Hospital. Developments there over some ten years have resulted in radical improvements in productivity, financial performance and morale – while at the same time financing new capital developments and service innovations. This is considerably influencing the planning of new organizational and budgeting arrangements at Lewisham and North Southwark, and possibly in other health authorities as well.

7.8    The logic of the comparison of the NHS against industrial financial models, together with the evidence from Dr Wickings' and other research such as that at St Thomas' Hospital reported by Jane Carter, led in 1978 to the team preparing the Perrin Report for the Royal Commission on the NHS to reach conlcusions very similar to the prescriptive recommendations reached by the Griffiths Inquiry in 1983. The 1978 conclusions were (paragraph C8.14):

> that the most promising development seems to be *specialty budgeting* supported by *specialty costing*, and that the purpose which might be served are as follows:
>
> (a)  better control of spending – by those making clinical decisions leading to the expenditure;
> (b)  incentive to efficiency – to achieve results at least cost;
> (c)  incentive to good *planning* and *budgeting* – considering the extra cost which extra cost output would require, compared with that in other parts of the hospital, district or area;
> (d)  incentive to production of good data output;
> (e)  production of figures at *cost* for each specialty, which would (i) allow comparison with other clinical firms or hospitals, and (ii) allow averaging to produce cost figures for strategic planning and for formation of national policies on health;

(f) allowing the clinician, and managers at various levels, to *compare results* of expenditure and output with *budgets* and operational *plans*.

Of course the above 1978 advice is not an exact match for Griffiths' 1983 recommendations. Griffiths prefers budgeting and costing to be at the level of the individual clinician rather than the whole specialty, and he introduces the word 'management' into the description, implying a more imperative style in the use of information in the constant quest for economy, efficiency and effectiveness.

## The Griffiths Recommendations

**7.9**   Most readers will know well the Griffiths (NHS Management) Inquiry Report and may indeed have a copy handy for reference, so there is little need to quote at length from the Report itself. Clearly to the press – and probably also to many readers – the most important topic covered in the Inquiry Report was that of general management, leading to recommendations to introduce the general manager at national, regional, district and unit levels – all this implying not just the creation of new posts, but rather and more critically the appointment of individuals who are intended to be held personally accountable for introducing a new sense of urgency into decision-making, performance assessment and control. However, there is also extensive discussion of budgeting and cost improvement within the Report. The Griffiths' recommendations on these matters may be summarized as follows:

a   There should be major cost improvement programmes, for implementation by general managers (paragraph 6.7).

b   District chairmen should involve clinicians more closely in the management process – in decisions about priorities in the use of resources. Clinicians need administrative support, together with strictly relevant management information, and a fully developed management budget approach. This approach should prompt some measurement of output in terms of patient care (paragraph 8.2).

c   District chairmen should see that each unit has a 'total budget' (a 'total budget' presumably means a budget which includes all indirect costs and overheads (see Chapter 3), for maximum consciousness at unit level of total resource use and cost, and to encourage interest in seeking all possible economies inclusive of proposing changes in resource use not under the immediate budgets or control at the unit itself) (paragraph 8.4).

d   District chairmen should ensure that district procedures spell out: the role of treasurers in providing management accounting support to unit managers (8.5.1); rules for virement between unit budgets and between individual budgets, including arrangements for the use of planned and unplanned savings (8.5.2); authorization limits and the flexible use of total resources (8.5.3); and the financial relationship between unit budgets and any district-wide budgets for functional services on which the unit may call (8.5.4). (The arrangements in this category are largely of a technical nature which treasurers would anyway see to automatically, irrespective of district chairmen, although the exact form of the arrangements would of course be adapted to the organizational structure and form of budgetary responsibility authorized by the individual health authority.)

e    District chairmen should ensure that 'each unit develops *management budgets*, which involve clinicians and relate work-load and service objectives to financial and manpower allocations, so as to sharpen up the questioning of overhead costs' (paragraph 8.6). (Here there may be an infelicity in the drafting of the Inquiry Report, since the main objective of management budgets must surely be to sharpen up the questioning of those costs budget holders directly control or strongly influence, not just 'overhead costs' which represent only a small fraction of total costs.)

f    The Chairman of the NHS Management Board should ensure that a 'property function' is developed to achieve commercial exploitation of the NHS estate (see also paragraph 28 of the 'Background to Recommendations') (10.1), and that procedures for handling major capital schemes and disposal of property are streamlined and provide maximum devolution from the centre (10.2). (These topics will be considered further in Chapter 8.)

g    The accountability review process is commended, and it needs to be extended to units of management, starting with a unit performance review based on management budgets which involve the clinicians at hospital level. Real output measurement, against clearly stated management objectives and budgets, should become a major concern of management at all levels (paragraph 7 of 'General Observations'). There is further emphasis for this in paragraph 19 of the 'Background to Recommendations', which states that doctors should 'be looked upon as the natural managers', and that this should be recognized in constructing the system of management budgets.

## *Are the Griffiths recommendations attainable?*

**7.10**    In this chapter we are directly concerned only with Griffiths' recommendations on clinical management budgets (CMBs). These recommendations involve the assumption that (at least eventually) all clinicians will be willing to assume responsibility for expenditure on those resources whose volume they control, and also to take an active interest in influencing the costs and efficiency of use of indirect resources and overheads which they do not  directly control.

We must now consider how far Griffiths' recommendations are realistic. This can be assessed in response to three separate questions:

1    Is there a sufficient managerial will to implement the Griffiths recommendations on clinical management budgets?
2    Is there a sufficient willingness among clinicians to assume the budgetary responsibilities, and the implicit concern for economy, efficiency and effectiveness, which Griffiths appear to seek to lay upon them?
3    Is the quality, i.e. the accuracy, timeliness and overall credibility, of the available financial and activity/workload information sufficient to

support a disciplined, effective introduction and use of clinical management budgets? Or if it is not, then what needs to be done, and how soon can it be done?

**7.11** It will depend upon the commitment of district general managers, and upon the unit general managers whom they in turn appoint, how far there will be a strong managerial will to implement CMBs. As we shall consider again later, it is quite possible for CMBs, i.e. budgets for each separate clinician, to exist on paper without there having to be any active, dynamic management by the individual clinician in making use of the budget for improving performance in relation to any of the Three Es (economy, efficiency and effectiveness). So the answer to Question 7.10(1) must be ambivalent for the time being.

**7.12** As regards the willingness of individual clinicians to assume responsibility for CMBs, one may look to the evidence from research into consultants' attitudes. Here the two main reported studies carried our recently in the UK are by Jane Carter at St Thomas' Hospital, including the views of functional budget holders in a parallel inquiry, and by the Operational Research Unit at the West Midlands Regional Health Authority on behalf of the Financial Information Project.

The author's own view is that both these studies, even though they appear to have been conducted with great care and propriety, and with rigour in analysing the findings, are quite inconclusive in the context of assessing the acceptability to clinicians of the recommendations of the Griffiths Inquiry. The reason for this is that the economic climate of the NHS (and of the country) has changed substantially since the two research projects were carried out, and also that the state of opinion and attitudes within the NHS itself may very likely have altered as a result of the Griffiths Inquiry Report, its findings, and the climate of opinion, press comment, etc., which followed in its wake.

**7.13** Our third question (7.10(3)) concerns whether or not the accuracy, timeliness (i.e. promptness of reporting after the end of the monthly (or other) control period) and relevance of the cost and activity information provided for each individual clinician will be sufficient to support a credible, disciplined, effective use of clinical management budgets. This question is of the essence to the central theme of this book: can NHS financial information be used to achieve more effective financial management of the limited resources available? We will leave the answer to emerge from later pages.

## Three approaches to clinical management budgeting

**7.14** There are three main approaches, as noted previously, to development of clinical management budgets, and we shall introduce these in turn. They comprise the Körner approach, the CASPE approach and the Griffiths approach. At the risk of gross oversimplification, we may attempt to characterize the differences in the three approaches. The Körner approach appears to aim to have all the supporting (i.e. 'feeder') activity, workload and costing systems set up and running accurately before introducing clinical budgeting. The CASPE approach appears to accept the importance of the underlying information systems but to give even greater importance to developing positive attitudes and interests among clinicians and managers prior to introducing clinical budgeting, and it stresses the planning aspects of budgets more than the control aspects. Lastly, the Griffiths approach appears to believe that the needs of the service for more efficient management of resources are so urgent that the upgrading of information systems, the motivation of clinicians and managers, and the introduction of clinical management budgeting must all progress simultaneously, with any problems discovered being debugged while development work continues without significant loss of credibility and motivation among clinicians and managers involved in the new budgets. In the following sections we explore the differences between the three approaches in more detail, and we explain briefly how each approach is being implemented and tested.

## The Körner approach

**7.15** We have noted previously that the Final Report on Financial Information from the Körner Steering Group on Health Service Information includes a code of practice for good budgeting. It also includes a number of passing references to clinicians in its discussion of budgeting in the NHS, although it is not clear from the context if these references were meant to apply beyond the role clinicians already often have as budget holders for diagnostic or other service departments. The only explicit reference to the more general involvement of clinicians as budget holders occurs in the passage from which we have previously quoted.

Taking all the reports from the Steering Group together, the overall message from Körner would appear to be that there is enormous work to be done in the NHS in installing consistent, accurate and relevant 'feeder systems' of activity and workload information, and in getting specialty costing to work reliably and promptly in reporting costed activity/workload output – before any attempt is made to introduce clinical budgeting as an operational system. The concern appears to be that the premature erection of a superstructure of clinical budgets upon inadequate foundations of activity/workload and cost information might bring the whole exercise of upgrading NHS management information into disrepute.

**7.16** Each area of information, minimum data sets and reporting recommended in the several Körner interim reports was piloted for feasibility, relevance and acceptability in several health districts during the consultation period preceding each final report from Körner. And the Körner Steering Group was kept well informed on the progress of research and trials on Magee (specialty costing), CASPE (planning agreements and budgets with clinicians) and FIP (information modules for patient costing in the hospital and in the community). Towards the end of the main Körner programme of reports it was decided to organize a major project in one district to test and demonstrate the working of the Körner recommendations. This was funded by the DHSS under the title of the Management

Information Pilot Project (MIPP) and was placed in Bromsgrove and Redditch Health Authority (with the assistance of Price Waterhouse Associates as management consultants).

From the point of view of scientific inquiry it would have been useful if this project had been arranged quite independently of the other two approaches, as a 'control'. However, the MIPP started too late for this degree of independence, and its terms of reference required it to take account of the NHS Management Inquiry and to report to the Steering Group on Management Budgets (i.e. the steering committee for the demonstration projects under the Griffiths approach). It therefore seems likely that there will have been pressure for the MIPP to move to the clinical budgeting stage fairly quickly, regardless of whether or not all the subsets of Körner information have yet been perfected. The report of Price Waterhouse Associates to the DHSS dated 20 December 1983 is lengthy and thorough in assessing the state of existing data, systems and computerization in Bromsgrove and Redditch District for meeting Körner information requirements, and in setting out the development work needed.

*The CASPE approach*

**7.17**   Dr Iden Wickings devised innovational research into the involvement of consultants and other front-line staff in the use of planning, budgeting and costing information during his service as an administrator in Westminster and Brent health districts. The essential findings from these projects have been mentioned previously: the results from Westminster indicated that planning agreements in the form of budgets, including the right to redeploy underspendings (i.e. savings) into other uses, could secure greater economy and efficiency. In contrast, the research at Brent over three years using specialty costing information alone, without budgets, yielded no evidence that the clinical teams participating in the project improved economy or efficiency any more than did the control teams not participating.

Since 1979 Dr Wickings has been Director of CASPE (Clinical Accountability, Service Planning and Evaluation) based at the King Edward's Hospital Fund. CASPE has initiated research in several fields, but its main work is in assisting clinicians (and sometimes associated senior nurses and other colleagues as a 'team') to become involved in resource planning, costing and budgeting exercises. These exercises have become known as PACTS (Planning Agreements of Clinical Teams).

**7.18**   Recent CASPE projects involving clinicians in resource planning, costing and budgeting have been organized, with DHSS support and funding, in Oldham, Southend, and Lewisham and North Southwark. References to the CASPE approach later in this chapter will be based mainly on the plans and progress at Lewisham and North Southwark. Although the latter is one of the newest of the CASPE projects, it is also the best funded and most highly computerized, so that it is perhaps the only CASPE project which may be compared fairly with the well funded projects testing the Körner approach and the Griffiths approach. The newest CASPE project has started at Brighton Health Authority, aiming to introduce clinical budgeting linked to the provision of a quality assurance programme.

### The Griffiths Inquiry approach

**7.19** The Griffiths Inquiry Report in several passages strongly commends the use of management budgeting in the NHS, to involve clinicians and to relate workload and service objectives to financial and manpower allocations. The importance attached to this is evidenced by the following statement from paragraph 8.6 of the Report: 'This (i.e. management budgeting) is such a vital management tool that the Inquiry has already set up demonstrations in four District Health Authorities, under a joint Inquiry/DHSS/NHS Steering Group, which will maintain the impetus and stimulate wider implementation pending the appointment of the NHS Management Board to drive through this initiative.'

The emphasis here may surprise readers who know that the NHS already operates under budgetary control. But clearly Griffiths did not consider the present NHS budgeting to be adequate. Griffiths' use of the term 'management budgets' repeatedly where just 'budgets' might suffice, gives a clear signal of the Inquiry team's views. Except for some budgets for ancillary services, NHS budgets are normally operated as 'controls on expenditure' rather than as 'management tools'. That is, decisions on how much money to budget, and on the reasonableness of the later outturn of expenditure against budget, are not usually related to measured workloads or specific service objectives.

Especially is this so at the level of clinical services, which inevitably provide the 'engine' generating pressure on resources and expenditure throughout the system. Hence the Griffiths prescription that clinicians should become budget holders, and that all other service costs and overheads should be redistributed to the clinical budgets, so that clinicians can see, react to, and influence the economy, efficiency and effectiveness of the total health care delivery system.

**7.20** Readers who do not know the NHS well might feel that the Griffiths call to involve clinicians in management budgeting is an indictment of the existing financial management of the NHS. To some extent this may be the case, although we must note that this is perhaps the first time in the history of the NHS that an agent of the government has called out firmly for the combination of better financial information, the involvement of clinicians in detailed resource management, and an investment in management skills and computers to make all this possible. Past guidance from government in these areas has appeared to be largely restricted to pressure to reduce or limit management costs, and to make do with such information as could be derived from very slowly evolving regional mainframe computer installations and standard systems. And indeed, the degree of improvement in NHS financial and workload information for routine managerial and clinical accountability which Griffiths now calls for, would probably have been quite impracticable and uneconomic without the advent and adoption of the cheap microcomputers which have only recently become available.

**7.21** Nor has Britain been alone in having inadequate financial systems which failed to relate clinical workload with the detail of expenditure, or to make clinicians financially accountable. This has been true in most countries, although growing concern over the high costs of health care, and improving skill in analysis and in the application of computer information systems, are leading other countries towards similar developments as in the Griffiths clinical management budgets.

Nor is this the end of information and systems development: progress with the analysis of clinical output using diagnosis related groupings (DRGs) or other systems of classifying and costing patients by case mix and case severity should allow more refined analysis of clinical management budgets within a few years (see Chapter 9 for details).

7.22   To accelerate progress and bring in additional skills, two firms of management consultants were appointed to assist in the management budgeting demonstrations, Arthur Young McClelland Moores & Co. (AYMM) assisting Southmead and North Tees health authorities, and Coopers & Lybrand Associates assisting Basingstoke and Ealing health authorities. Arthur Young additionally developed the software for the computer processing of budget data at the clinical level of analysis in all four demonstration districts. This same AYMM software, it is understood, has been adopted also in the MIPP at Bromsgrove and Redditch, as well as in the CASPE project at Lewisham and North Southwark. This should assist comparability.

7.23   Through using the same computer software and programs it seems likely that the format of budgets and budget reports from the four Griffiths demonstration districts will appear quite similar. However, there are differences of approach and priority between the two firms of management consultants, although it may be that the best from both approaches will be adopted in future into a standardized package of procedures to assist other districts starting management budgeting. Nevertheless, there will almost certainly be important differences among the four districts in the exact content of budgets which nominally appear comparable, and in the detail of the cost allocations or apportionments used to charge costs of budget headings. This seems almost inevitable not just because of differences in local organizational arrangements and responsibilities between districts, but also because the feeder systems for patient administration, manpower, pathology, radiology and pharmacy, etc., are at different stages of development and sophistication, are running on a variety of recording systems and in some cases are not yet fully computerized. These underlying differences need not seriously affect the value of using clinical management budgets within any one district, but they will mean that it may be unwise and unfair to attempt inter-district performance comparisons of clinical costs within specialties until a few years have elapsed to allow fuller computerization and standardization of the feeder systems.

*The timetable for clinical budgeting*

7.24   Clinical management budgets are not yet proven in any health district. This is not surprising since much preparatory work is required. The budget computer and software has to be ordered, installed and tested.

Every feeder system has to be evaluated, and if it is operated manually and is perhaps not very accurate because not previously used in management control (e.g. manpower information and patient administration systems), then new procedures have to be worked out for the collection, entry, checking and processing of data. Where the volume of data is great and is not yet efficiently computerized, then it may be necessary to instal effective computer support for the feeder systems before it is possible to obtain data for clinical budgeting and costing which is both sufficiently accurate *and* sufficiently quickly available as to allow budgetary performance reports to be completed and supplied to clinical and other budget holders without a demoralizing delay.

**7.25** The feeder systems most likely to require computerization as a precondition for the successful working of clinical management budgeting are detailed in 7.27 below. Parallel to the development or computerization of improved 'feeder system' information, work must go forward in arousing the interest of clinicians in the new systems, and generally in explanation and education for all affected by clinical management budgets, which includes staff working on the feeder systems, finance staff, and all existing budget holders, additional to the new clinical budget holders. Also, procedures have to be agreed between clinicians, the UMG, the finance department and district management as regards important arrangements such as specifying rights of virement and who can determine the redeployment of savings – two important motivational issues to which we return again later.

**7.26** When most of the above tasks have been completed, the new computerized management budget system should be ready to start producing clinical management costs to match each intended clinical budget. These costs will normally be supplied monthly and over a period of months will provide insight into the resource usage of consultants, such as can form the basis for future agreed budgets. Any errors in the tracing of costs and workloads to particular budget centres can also be identified and corrected during this period.

Six months may be an adequate period for running in monthly cost reporting against intended new budget centres. But preferably a year should be allowed for this, both so as to capture all annual seasonal factors affecting workload and demands on resources, and also to allow more time for rectifying weaknesses in feeder systems. Finally, the new clinical budgets (and the new form of service department and facilities budgets) can be brought into use, preferably in April at the start of the new financial year in the health authority.

In the first year the new budgets will presumably be run in parallel with the old functional budgets, as a safeguard against any breakdown of cash expenditure control and also to allow any remaining weaknesses in the costing and budgeting assumptions, and in the allocations to clinical management budgets, to be detected and rectified. Then, all being well, the new budget system can take over fully from the old, at a point roughly two to three years from the first start of development on the new budgets and their supporting feeder systems. Figure 7.1 gives a diagrammatic summary

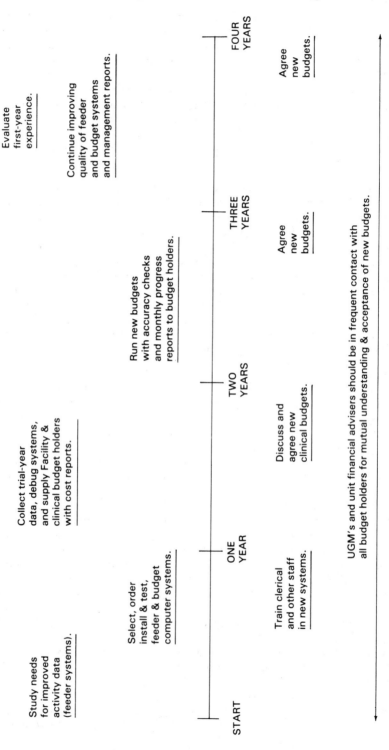

Fig. 7.1   Time-scale for introducing clinical budgeting.

of the time-scale planning problems for introducing clinical management budgeting.

*Computerization needed for clinical management budgets*

**7.27** Prior to drafting this book, the author had discussions at six of the eight health authorities participating in the three approaches to clinical budgeting reviewed in this chapter. In every case but one, the arrangements for the visits were made by the treasurers, and the author is grateful for the time and co-operation which both treasurers and project staff so willingly gave. There was a high degree of unanimity as regards the identification of which feeder systems need to be computerized before clinical budgeting can become effective, with accurate and up-to-date cost reports set against budget allocations. All agreed that pathology, radiology and patient administration needed to be computerized, and most included pharmacy as well.

But of course this is only the starting line. Eventually – and the sooner the better – all NHS information systems involving the processing of large volumes of data will need to be computerized, not just for accuracy and promptness in the supply of information for budgetary and other management controls, but also because this is the most economical method of processing such data. Included in this will be data on manpower (establishments, in-post, vacancies, overtime and special payments and (perhaps most importantly) absenteeism), and also data on the workloads of the smaller diagnostic and paramedical service departments not covered in initial computerization. Naturally, computers will also play an expanding role in monitoring the workload and resource use in ancillary services which are not privatized – for example in recording the activities and costs of works staff, and of energy utilization.

# Motivation and participation of clinicians

**7.28** A concern of many researchers and commentators on the NHS, including the author of this book during his work for the Royal Commission in 1977–78, has been regarding whether or not NHS consultants could ever be persuaded to accept individually, as distinct from collectively and amorphously, a share in the financial control and accountability of the NHS. The traditional argument had been that responsibility for obtaining the best care available for individual patients – clinical autonomy – prevented clinicians from participating directly in financial or other resource control systems which might conflict with, or override, their clinical responsibilities. Nevertheless, it is obvious that the financial resources of the NHS have always been limited, even if the pressure from this is much more obvious nowadays than during the first three decades of the NHS.

**7.29** There has always been a waiting list in the NHS, because resources have been inadequate to meet demand for a free service. It is not new for clinicians to need to restrict renal treatment to (relatively) younger patients, to need to tolerate lengthening queues for hip replacements, or even to have to exercise discretion in deciding which patients need a simple hernia operation sooner than others on grounds of occupational and social circumstances. The question now must be: has the reduction in the average national growth rate of the NHS to a rate only approximately equalling the growing needs of an ageing population – but with national and regional redistributions on grounds of equity resulting in many districts literally having to cut spending in real-terms – created a new environment in which clinicians are more willing to share in responsibility for how health care resources are utilized? Hopefully, there are signs that there is such a new environment – in which a majority of consultants will accept that the NHS should be managed to provide 'the greatest good for the greatest number'.

**7.30** Enunciating 'the greatest good for the greatest number' is easier to state, than it is to make explicit in determining who most needs which treatment, given the resources available and the relative costs of different treatments. Certainly the absence of firm information on the comparative costs of treating one type of condition as compared to another makes it more difficult for clinicians and others to decide on the best use of resources. Also the lack of budgets for individual clinicians (or for firms or specialties where clinicians prefer to organize their work together in teams), and the lack of routinely available expenditure costs to measure progress against budgets, has meant that decisions on the best use of resources have had to be made intuitively rather than on objective evidence and substantiated debate.

Now the development of clinical management budgets may for the first time provide the needed 'objective evidence', and it is to be hoped that the medical professions will welcome this and make good use of the new information to determine the best use of NHS treatment facilities, as well as helping in identifying potential economics which could conserve funds for redeployment into priority treatment services.

*BMA views on management budgeting*

**7.31** On 7 March 1984 the Chairman of CCHMS within the British Medical Association (BMA) circulated a letter to chairmen of medical executive committees on the subject of 'management budgeting'. Following explanatory paragraphs regarding the Griffiths Inquiry and the clinical management budgeting demonstrations arising from the Inquiry, the letter noted that clinicians taking on management budgeting responsibilities would have a profound effect on consultant's work, but the CCHMS hoped that it will be able to encourage consultants to take on these responsibilities, 'as this will lead to control of clinical services remaining firmly in the hands of clinicians'. However, to justify the above encouragement the CCHMS felt that a number of conditions must first be satisfied. The conditions specified were as follows:

(1)  Consultants should not accept responsibility for clinical budgets unless they are able to exert influence over all aspects of those budgets.
(2)  The practice of management budgeting depends entirely upon the active co-operation of clinicians.
(3)  The quality of financial information available in the health service must be improved significantly before it is reasonable to ask clinicians to take

responsibility for their own budgets. Until such an improvement is demonstrated the CCHMS will not be encouraging consultants to take responsibility for budgets.

(4) Consultants should not be joint budget holders with non-medical staff.
(5) Individual consultants should be answerable on budgetary matters only to the clinicians on the unit management team.
(6) Budget holders in departments of pathology and radiology must be consultants.

**7.32** In general the CCHMS conditions do not appear to be insuperable but two or three comments may be in order. First, condition (1) over-simplifies the real-life situation where it may be expected that clinical budgets will be subdivided between (a) the direct costs over which consultants exercise control or strong influence (e.g. on the volume of diagnostic tests), (b) the indirect costs over which they may have some influence (e.g. ward and other facilities costs, and the fixed costs (i.e. size) of service departments, and (c) the overhead costs over which they exercise little influence except collectively through medical advisory machinery and clinical representation on unit and district management teams. The *managerial* accountability imposed on consultants for budgetary performance would only be in respect of the first of the above three categories.

Secondly, regarding condition (3), it must be accepted that the financial (or more precisely, the activity and workload) information used in the NHS for budgeting must be improved: this is indeed an objective of the Griffiths' demonstrations, and it is given even greater priority in the Körner and CASPE projects, as well as in the work of the FIP.

Finally, condition (5) involves individual consultants being answerable on budgets only to 'clinicians on the unit management team'. This condition could be a bit awkward, but of course we do not yet know how the appointment of unit general managers will in the long term affect the roles of unit management groups or teams, nor how often consultants themselves will in future take on the unit general manager role and thus facilitate the entry of clinicians generally into senior roles of financial responsibility for the use of NHS resources.

In any event, nothing which is currently proposed should be seen as threatening the clinical autonomy of consultants in deciding the best uses of available resources in treating individual patients.

*Further complications*

**7.33** To the extent that some clinical odium has settled on CMBs, this should be evaluated objectively. CMBs should be evaluated on their own merits and not because of any dislike of the more organizationally oriented reforms demanded by Griffiths for general management and a more business-style approach to management. Nor should CMBs be blamed for pressing on clinical resources when the true sources of such pressure arise from the combined effects of governmental restraint on the level of NHS funding, and of the redistributive effects of RAWP applied nationally and within regions.

So, CMBs should be seen as society's response to dealing with a 'problem', and not as the problem itself. So long as there is an apparent shortage of resources for health care – which could mean forever, literally – one means or another will be sought by governments to improve the efficiency of health care delivery, and also to adjust the allowed 'ration' of scarce health care resources to alternative care groups increasingly on the basis of client/public/political choices rather than on the basis of clinical preferences. CMB is one vehicle in an optimizing process by which clinicians have the opportunity to gain better information for making choices – and also for 'arguing their corner' with unit and district management (and with the local and national public opinions which provide the management with their authority to enforce choices).

**7.34**   Clinicians and others have sometimes been critical of the installation and running costs of CMB systems, relative to the expected benefits. Certainly the author's impression from informal discussions with staff in districts pioneering CMB is that the start-up costs over the first two or three years are likely to exceed half a million pounds per district. But up to 80 % of this outlay is likely to be on upgrading and computerizing feeder systems, i.e. activity/workload recording and measurement systems, which would be needed anyway to meet accurately and efficiently Körner information standards or to provide the prompt and accurate information which doctors, nurses and service department heads would wish to have to monitor the workload under their own personal control. And once these CMB supporting feeder systems are up and running successfully, the ongoing costs are not likely to be much higher, if any higher, than previously. The reason is that, once established, efficiently designed and efficiently controlled computerized information systems are more economical of clerical labour cost than the old fashioned manual systems. Computerization of NHS information systems has been inevitable, as in other large organizations – the advent of CMB has hastened the inevitable.

**7.35**   For much of the time since the initiation of the Griffiths CMB demonstration projects, senior members of the nursing and paramedical professions have been at least as doubtful and critical of CMB as have been medical and surgical clinicians. Partly this may be because the effect of the Griffiths organizational reforms appeared to be to devalue the relative status and independence of all other professions working in the NHS relative to the new general managers, the clinical consultants, and possibly the finance staff. This bred a sense of frustration and insecurity.

But also partly it was because of the notion that senior nurses and paramedicals would no longer be 'user budget holders' in their own right (or so it appeared), but instead mere 'intermediate budget holders' whose budgets/costs would be recharged to CMBs. One implication was that clinical consultants, holders of CMBs, might seek to cut their use of nursing or paramedical services, in turn forcing these services to cut their staffing, or to cut their standards. Hopefully the CMB demonstration trials will have served to prove these doubts and criticisms unnecessary.

Certainly the author's experience from research and trials other than Griffiths' CMB is that on the whole nurses and paramedicals have demonstrated markedly greater interest than consultants in respect of holding budgets, and receiving and using cost and other performance information.

And after all, if eminent radiologists and pathologists have accepted inter-mediate budget status for their service departments, it cannot be demeaning for nursing and paramedical professionals to do the same.

7.36 The other reason why some nurses and many paramedicals have protested at the Griffiths CMB model is because the Griffiths model assumed that consultant doctors were the only user budget holders in the hospital service. Senior paramedical staff, in particular, argue that they are clinicians in their own right. Hospital doctors may refer patients to them for treatment, but usually the volume and form of treatment is determined by the paramedical experts. In addition, in many districts a high proportion of the cases treated by paramedical departments is referred to them by the pri-mary and community services (or directly by patients who walk in off the street), so that it is quite illogical to recharge the costs of such care to the CMBs of hospital consultants.

In the author's opinion by now most treasurers involved with CMBs have been persuaded of the justice of the above argument. Certainly there are no technical reasons why the standard cost of one or more standard treatments from paramedical staff cannot be recharged to consultant CMBs, with the ramainder of paramedical treatment costs being retained in the para-medical budgets as 'end user' budgets in their own right. Getting the balance right is simply a matter of experiment and experience.

## Conclusions

7.37 CMB offers great promise in terms of information likely to be useful to clinicians, and to unit general managers acting as 'ringholders' seeking to optimize the total output of services provided from limited resources. There are, however, important obstacles to the rapid achievement of successful CMB systems in practice. There are behavioural problems for clinicians in accepting accountability and discipline for the costs of the resources they cause to be consumed in aiding patients. There are behavioural problems for the nursing and paramedical professions in accepting the Griffiths assumption (of which CMBs with hospital doctors as the only 'user' budget holders is but one illustration) that consultant doctors are the natural managers of the total hospital services. There are financial problems in terms of the limited resources available for the rapid upgrading and compu-terization of activity or workload information systems capable of supporting an accurate clinical budgeting system with prompt reporting of performance/variances at monthly intervals. There are staffing problems as regards providing sufficient skilled unit financial advisers (or management accountants), given current NHS salary scales and constraints on manage-ment costs and grading structures.

But these are all problems which should be resolved in time, with good management. And to ignore or to seek to fend off CMBs may be likened to the gamesmanship of King Canute. The pressure for better performance monitoring information from many quarters, and the feasibility of this with ever cheaper and more efficient computing systems, combine to act like the rising tide: sand castles may be built upon the beaches, but sooner or later the rising tide will erode them. The moral of all this is that it may well be in the interests of NHS consultants and other professions to co-operate actively/in shaping CMB and other new financial resource information control, costing and budgetary systems, rather than to waste their energy building sand castles to delay the rising tide, slightly.

# Summary

1 Clinical management budgeting (CMB) is the next evolutionary stage of NHS financial information development beyond specialty costing. CMB involves hospital consultants taking a share of responsibility in planning and monitoring the distribution and use of hospital resources among the different specialties or individual clinicians. Historically doctors have not sought this role, although willing to take part collectively through advisory committees and representation on management teams and authority boards.

2 The Griffiths Inquiry Report said that clinicians were the 'natural managers' of hospital services. Each unit should have its own overall management budgets in which clinicians should be involved. But to achieve this, clinicians would need administrative support and a supply of strictly relevant management information. To show the feasibility and benefit of this approach, four 'demonstration districts' were given extra funding from late 1983 to develop CMBs at the level of the individual clinician or specialty.

3 CMB is not a new idea. The testing of specialty budgeting was recommended in the late Royal Commission's Research Paper No. 2 of 1978. Since 1979 the CASPE projects have been researching the involvement of clinicians in financial planning and the search for savings and useful redeployments of resources. The emphasis in CASPE was on winning the interest and co-operation of doctors, but there were problems because of inadequate data in the 'feeder' systems' and costing information. The Griffiths demonstration districts set out to computerize feeder systems and costing to overcome the latter problem. Meanwhile, the Körner reports gave impetus to improving the quality of workload and activity information feeder systems – but resources were not always available to computerize these to a level of accuracy and prompt reporting capable of supporting monthly CMB progress reports. Körner did not directly recommend CMB.

4 Since 1985 many additional districts have started on developing CMB. Two official demonstration districts for management budgeting in the community have reportedly progressed well – as has MIPP, a project inspired by Körner. But progress in the CMBs for acute services has been patchy. The difficulties of introducing CMBs in hospitals seemingly were underestimated.

5 It takes at least three or four years to introduce a working CMB system in hospitals. All patient administration, activity and workload information and costing systems have to be upgraded to at least the new Körner standards, the major systems have to be computerized, and it takes six to twelve months to test the new systems and collect sufficient activity and costs data to form the basis for setting clinical budgets. Then the new budgets must be 'run' for at least one trial year before evaluation.

# CHAPTER 8
# Resource management: revenue and capital

**8.1**   Chapter 7 was drafted before November 1986, during the period in which orthodox opinion (in spite of growing rumours) was that the DHSS expected Griffiths-style CMBs to prove themselves worthy of spreading rapidly through the NHS. This orthodoxy was 'put into the deep freeze' from November 1986 by the issue of HN(86)34, inaugurating the new era of 'resource management' – a wider, more participative concept which is to be driven or led by the interests of doctors, nurses and other professionals, rather than by the mechanics of information and accounting systems. However, it was decided to leave Chapter 7 largely unaltered from the earlier draft, to present the technical and largely positive case for CMBs, partly because aspects of CMBs will probably be incorporated in at least some of the 'new model pilot sites' for resource management, and partly because the author feels that sooner or later some future minister will resurrect CMBs from the deep freeze, and it is suspected that CMBs (under whatever new label) will prove to be in general use – and probably accepted and uncontroversial use – in the NHS before the end of the century.

**8.2**   This chapter opens by attempting to explain why Griffiths-style CMBs have not yet proved successful. It then considers what is involved in the new initiative on 'resource management'. Next a 'family tree' is constructed to show how various research and ministerial initiatives are converging to make possible management information support systems of greater relevance and value. Finally, we look at the use of capital in the NHS, its costs, option appraisal, and why and how capital issues should be included in at least some of the new initiatives in resource management.

## The rise and fall of CMBs

**8.3**   From the early 1970s, if not before, perceptive thinkers could foresee that the NHS would enter into ever increasing difficulty in meeting the needs, or certainly the expectations, of the public in respect of their health care. The costs would exceed what governments would be willing, or perhaps even able, to fund. Arguably the 1974 reorganization was oblivious to this problem and largely served simply to increase bureaucracy and make decision-making more remote from the sharp end of health care.

The 1982 reorganization at least partly remedied some of these problems. But even that reorganization left intact the 'functional management' ethos from prior years: the idea that the NHS was best run by consensus and the pooling together of authority by the leaders of various professions (or functions) meeting together as equals at each level of management organization. This pattern of management was naturally suspect to a government dedicated to introducing business-style management and efficiency to public bodies. Hence the (Griffiths) NHS Management Inquiry.

**8.4** The primary theme of the Griffiths Report was the need to change from consensus/functional management to leadership by general managers at all levels down to units. The author believes that future historians of the NHS will conclude that the change to general management represented a marked improvement, although that verdict will depend on good selection, training and support for general managers at all levels. A secondary theme of the Griffiths Report was the need to inculcate, monitor and enforce a tougher managerial ethos at all levels of professional or functional management/leadership below the new general managers.

Almost as a by-product of this secondary theme, in the author's opinion, the Griffiths Inquiry noted that NHS financial control systems were primarily devoted simply to keeping cash spending within authorized limits. The NHS financial information systems provided little information which was suitable to monitor the cost-efficiency of functional managers – while clinicians, the engines driving resource consumption, were left almost entirely without financial information or accountability for their resources, workload and performance. The Griffiths Report concluded, quite rationally in 'business' terms, that this situation should be remedied.

**8.5** Thus Griffiths recommended that (business-style) management budgets should be developed down to the level of individual clinicians, the natural managers of the hospital services. Their advice appears to have been that most clinicians would welcome, or at least amicably accept, this new innovation. And indeed that might have been the outcome – in spite of rearguard protests about interference with clinical autonomy and the waste of high-paid time on matters of financial housekeeping – if the demonstration districts developing the new Griffiths clinical management budgets (CMBs) had been able to deliver quickly the kind of 'all singing, all dancing' sophisticated budget information and management systems which the Griffiths Inquiry team presumably had in mind when making their strong endorsements of CMBs. So, what went wrong?

**8.6** In one of the four first-generation CMB demonstration districts it appears that the computer systems support proved to be quite inadequate (and this is not necessarily to be blamed wholly or even mainly on local management). In the other three demonstration districts the lack of visible success in introducing CMBs appears to be put down, broadly, to failure to interest, involve and commit the large majority of clinical staff needed the enable CMBs to have a major, positive impact on improving resource utilization. Behind this generalization there may be a number of fundamental difficulties which the Griffiths Inquiry and the DHSS did not adequately foresee.

First, the CMB demonstrations were started (September 1983) at a time of 'organizational turbulence' before the new unit general managers were fully in post and had resolved the new management structures within units (or appointed staff thereto). Secondly, it seems probable that the Griffiths team did not appreciate the order of magnitude by which the variety and number of flows of separately identified consumables and services in a large hospital exceeds the comparable flows in a biscuit factory or a supermarket. (In technical terms, the latter two types of organizations will have large volumes of cost flowing in parallel accountability tracks, but little cross-switching between tracks, unlike the NHS.) Thirdly, but related to the second point, the Griffiths team probably did not realize how far the often simple manual recording procedures in the NHS designed as minimum-cost (although often labour-intensive) systems to monitor and control expenditure against functional budgets would prove incapable of supporting the degree of accuracy and speed needed to support a cost recharging system to user budget holders (i.e. clinicians).

**8.7** Fourthly, Griffiths overestimated the speed with which professional independence could be supplanted by a disciplined management culture led by general management. It appears still to be the case, in the NHS, that change has to be effected by persuasion and often by tedious negotiation, rather than by dictate based on 'this is what the boss/general manager/health authority wants done'. For example, this author has observed at first hand the frustrations of staff attempting to introduce, over a period of years, first specialty costing, and then CMB. These systems innovations need good computerized feeder systems, capable of relating items of resource use to individual specialties or consultants. Time and again the author has seen decisions on, or action on, these feeder systems delayed by hospital committees, district committees, or apparent prevarication from the region concerned.

It would appear that an important factor in this history of delay was the underlying problem of who would pay for the new computer systems, the district or the region! Of course, in the first-generation districts most of the cost of new computer systems was met from earmarked DHSS funding for the project, but it is not yet clear that even this extra funding was sufficient to resolve all the feeder-system data management problems.

**8.8** Fifthly, Griffiths underestimated the skilled manpower resources needed, or available, to implement as complex an innovation as CMB quickly. NHS districts employ many indians (clerks) but few chiefs (professionally qualified accountants). Management staffing and cost controls restrict the number of senior accounting or finance posts to a level far below the levels often found in the private sector. Nor are the NHS salary levels competitive to retain many first class accountants (below treasurer level) other than those who soldier on from blind loyalty. (And similar comments can be made regarding computer systems analysts and programmers. The NHS is not being allowed to adapt to market forces.) But of course the introduction of new systems as radical and complex as CMB requires two very different types of skill: first, skill with data collection and recording systems and their computerization, and secondly skill in dealing with people – and with consultants, in particular, in the context of CMBs.

The major criticisms of development of CMBs in the demonstration districts centre upon the failure of local management to give a sufficiently high priority to the CMB programme, especially as regards the communication and training needs of *all* staff to be involved – that is general managers, clinicians, nurses, and paramedical and other department heads, *as well as* the accounting and clerical staff. As we demonstrated in Chapter 7, it takes at least two or three years to establish a full CMB reporting system. During this time the natural instinct of accounting and computing staff is to concentrate solely or mainly on the systems design, data collection and computing aspects of the projects (i.e. those activities shown above the time-scale line in Fig. 7.1). Only firm leadership from general managers and the treasurer would be likely to overcome this tendency. Meanwhile, with clinicians and other intended budget holders left largely in a vacuum of information and understanding about CMBs, it is natural for them to begin to worry that CMBs may not turn out to be useful to them, but instead prove to be a time-wasting distraction or, at worst, a future vehicle for imposing and monitoring spending cuts.

## Resource management

**8.9**   The preceding section draws on HN(86)34 (p. 2) as regards what has gone wrong in many or most of the CMB development sites, although the author has added further, personal criticisms of his own. But of course the main part of HN(86)34 is not concerned with the old concept of CMBs, but with the way forward into a new, wider strategy of 'resource management'. Whereas CMBs turned out to be largely 'information system driven', the new approach is to be 'information user driven'. That is, the new series of resource management experiments (at six sites, at least initially) are to take place only at 'hospitals where doctors and nurses are already centrally involved in the management process'. And the experiments will centre around developing and using information which doctors and nurses themselves think will help them better to organize and manage their work. Patient case mix planning and costing is understood to be an area of strong interest for clinicians, and which is likely to be included in some of the experiments (and which is discussed further in Chapter 9).

**8.10**   HN(86)34 seems likely to represent, at least until late 1988, the DHSS's definitive guidance to the NHS regarding the form and pace of development of new financial information systems involving clinicians and other health care professions. By 1988 it is hoped that the 'new model' resource management approach will have proved itself, to the extent that implementation in other acute units could follow during the period 1988–92.

HN(86)34 has to be studied together with a joint statement of the national Joint Consultants Committee (JCC) and the NHS Management Board. This joint statement expands, tactfully, on the reasons why clinicians were disappointed by the outcomes to date of the original Griffiths CMB demonstrations. It extends JCC support, for the present, only to the six experimental trials listed in both the joint statement and the Health Notice. It implies that any further future co-operation on the expansion of clinical involvement in financial information systems and control will be dependent on success in the initial six trials.

However, the joint statement does not obstruct the DHSS from continuing development work in the existing first- and second-generation CMB sites (or other sites). And in return, the Health Notice makes it clear that the Management Board will encourage further work in the CMB sites only where these seek to conform with the new policy of developing financial information and control systems around the principles included in the Health Notice and joint statement, including the notion of 'medical and nursing "ownership" of the system'. The latter terminology is somewhat vague, and it could indeed become the basis for future argument over interpretation and application.

**8.11** The Health Notice estimates that each new model resource management development could cost between £400,000 and £600,000, about 70% of which can be met from central funds. But of course the DHSS expects a benefit to the Service from this outlay, and this is specified as an overall target of releasing at least one per cent of annual expenditure for redeployment on patient services. Presumably it will be for each district, through the usual consultative processes, to decide how far the redeployment of financial savings within acute units may be retained in those units to enhance the volume or quality of services provided, or how far the redeployment will involve transferring some portions of savings to the priority areas in community care.

**8.12** HN(86)34 reports also on an extension of the resource management approach into a second generation of projects in the community health services, with further support from central funds. The first-generation community management budgeting pilots (at Bromley and Worcester) have apparently gone well and not aroused the degree of anxiety experienced at the Griffiths acute sites.

From an information systems point of view the above result is unexpected, as it has been widely held that the typical recording systems for workload, use of time and of consumables, etc., was worse in the community than in hospitals. But this appears to have been outweighed in the community management budgeting pilots by some combination of good management and a culture or current climate of opinion which is more receptive than in acute units.

Here note that it is easier for staff to feel co-operative in the community sector which has been given priority for growth, than in the acute sector which in the majority of districts is being asked to mark time, or even to contract, in resource terms. Secondly, the organization structure of service delivery in the community is much less complex than in hospitals, with consultant doctors little involved and the leading roles taken by nursing and paramedical professions. By and large these latter groups have appeared to be more receptive to management ideas and techniques, and more interested in using financial information, than have the majority of hospital doctors.

**8.13** Returning to the acute units, it is clear that the DHSS no longer takes it on faith that business-style management budgeting is easily or automatically transferable into hospitals, at least at the level of involving consultants as accountable budget holders. But that should change in time, if the new experiments are successful. What is clear, however, is that the new resource management experiments are going to be closely watched by the clinical professions. By joint protocol with the JCC it has been agreed that the first six pilots will be rigorously evaluated from the point of view of their helpfulness to doctors and nurses in providing patient care and sharing in the management of resources in their unit. An affirmative evaluation is a precondition for any later and further expansion of financial/resource management control systems which would directly involve clinicians.

Thus in effect the original Griffiths CMB initiative is having to restart, with the doctors holding the 'abort' button. In the long run this may not be a bad development. Arguably the attempt to introduce CMB simultaneously with general management reorganization, and before the Körner data systems and new initiatives in workload and patient activity data computerization had come on stream, was an act of gross (political) over-optimism from the DHSS. But that is a comment made with the benefit of hindsight.

## Recap of financial resource management developments

**8.14** The new approach to 'resource management' (RM), the pause to rethink the best way forward, and the widening of CMB to take account of other sources of information, or methods of analysis, than just the rather mechanistic approach of management budgeting creates the opportunity to combine useful parts from several of the research and systems developments of recent years. Figure 8.1 seeks to show, diagrammatically, how the four main NHS management information initiatives have developed and how they may be able to converge and thus strengthen the latest projects in RM and community services MB.

At the top of the chart are the three major initiatives which began more or less simultaneously, not long after the reporting of the Royal Commission on the NHS. These are Körner (NHS/DHSS Steering Group on Health Services Information), CASPE (Clinical Accountability, Service Planning and Evaluation), and FIP (Financial Information Project). Slightly lower down the chart is Griffiths (NHS Management Inquiry) because it started much later than the others and was a 'short, sharp shock'.

CASPE was probably the first off the mark, with FIP close behind. Their work was primarily research, but with systems development for more general use also an objective. This involved continuing evolutionary work over a period of years right up to today. Körner's work involved 'banging heads together' within the NHS (and DHSS) to get agreement on a more

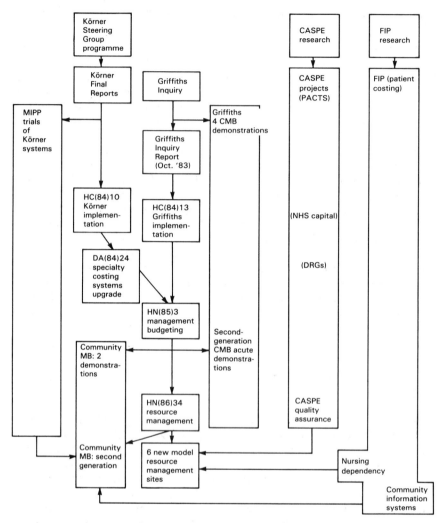

Fig. 8.1    Development and convergence of recent NHS financial information
systems.

useful (to local management) and uniform set of data collection and
reporting arrangements for financial, manpower and activity/workload
performance control information. Körner's work was nearly finished by the
time of the Griffiths Inquiry, although the workload in implementing
Körner will continue more or less until the end of this decade – and by that
time changes in NHS management, computing, and information needs may
justify a 'daughter of Körner' sequel inquiry.

**8.15**    Körner produced interim reports for consultation, and then Final
Reports. These were spread over 1982 through 1984. The Körner Sixth

Report, on financial data and reports, was one of the last to be published, in 1984. The Finance Final Report was much delayed from its interim report, and indeed it did not appear for some eight months after publication of the Griffiths Inquiry Report. One may speculate that the delay was caused by arguments concerning how far Körner should go in encouraging rapid progress towards clinical budgeting and/or patient costing.

The Griffiths Report appeared in October 1983, but weeks before that arrangements had already been put in train to start the four Griffiths CMB demonstrations. The implementation of Körner was authorized by HC(84)10, including target dates. Two months later HC(84)13 authorized implementation of the Griffiths Report recommendations. This included the development of management budgets but did not attempt to suggest a target date when CMB should become universal through the NHS. Then the first link between Körner and Griffiths appeared with DA(84)24 in effect requesting that authorities should develop (Körner) specialty costing at the higher level of sophistication which would be required for the eventual introduction of Griffiths' CMBs.

**8.16** At about the same time as the commissioning of the Griffiths CMB demonstrations, the DHSS also commissioned MIPP (the Management Information Pilot Project) at Bromsgrove and Redditch Health District to implement and test the recommendations of the Körner reports – this to cover both the acute and the community health services. It is the author's belief that the original brief did not include Griffiths' CMBs, but that later these came to be seen as a logical further development once all the Körner innovations had been mastered.

While MIPP went ahead gradually and with little publicity, the Griffiths CMB demonstration sites were encountering problems. The DHSS had acted very promptly on the Griffiths CMB recommendations, but until a year or more later when the new NHS Management Board became operational to include a Director of Financial Management, the DHSS lacked staff of relevant senior experience to monitor and advise on the progress of the CMB demonstrations. The DHSS then published HN(85)3 which effectively said 'We've got problems with CMB, but steady as we go'.

The key feature, which provides a link to HN(86)34 and the latest initiative on RM, was the now obvious awareness that CMB could not succeed purely as an information system imposed on clinicians and other health care professions: it must be tailored to their needs and they must be educated and advised in its use. And as we now know (from HN(86)34 if not also the grapevine) the latter requirements have not yet been fulfilled in the acute sector. HN(85)3 also announced the launch of community health MB, and a second generation of sites for CMB in acute units.

**8.17** Meanwhile, CASPE and FIP had been getting on with the job of conducting research and development, publicizing their work in a limited way through articles, progress reports and seminars from time to time, and also learning from experience of one cycle of research so as to start the next cycle at a deeper level. FIP's principal theme has been progress towards patient costing, and CASPE has become involved with DRGs (diagnosis related groups): these are developments considered in Chapter 9.

In the more immediate context of RM, new RM projects may well draw on FIP's work developing measurement and recording systems for nursing dependency, while both first- and second-generation community health MB projects may draw on FIP's experience in community workload and costing systems. CASPE projects have pioneered building financial and management information planning systems, starting from the interests of consultants and building outwards towards users' data requirements. These projects have been built upon PACTs (Planning Agreements of Clinical Teams), often including nurses with doctors. Arguably it is the CASPE model to which the DHSS's new model RM projects will need to look most closely for useful prior experience. Also the latest CASPE project, at Brighton, includes the important dimension of quality assurance analysis and review.

However, it would seem to be fair comment to suggest that not all CASPE PACT-based projects have been highly successful. It is the same old story (i.e. as with Griffith's CMBs), that is sometimes a few leading consultants attract a project and get actively involved, but prove unable to persuade the majority of their clinical peers to take part. And sometimes the financial resources available for information systems development to be able to respond to consultants' curiosity and information needs has been totally inadequate. But at one CASPE site, Guy's Hospital in London, there is advanced information computerization and (for the UK) a novel and advanced approach to clinical involvement in management. As Guy's is now one of the six new RM sites as well, with the extra financial and advisory support that should bring, this is the acute site with the greatest potential for demonstrating how the clinical and related professions should become actively and successfully involved in resource management.

## Developing resource management

8.18   We have yet to see what the new post-Griffiths resource management (RM) pilot projects will comprise. Presumably, with the eventual JCC evaluation looming in the background, they will not consist of veiled attempts to reintroduce CMB through the back door. The author, as it happens, supports the concept of CMB – but in the light of experience believes it would be ill advised to attempt to return to the full concept of CMB – that is, the notion that all consultants will hold formal budgets and be accountable for the NHS expenditure they cause to be incurred, just like business managers – until such time as all the Körner management information systems improvements have been fully implemented, tested, audited and found to be working accurately and efficiently. Indeed it is a moot point whether or not clinicians should be asked to hold budgets until such time as reliable patient costing or case mix costing systems are routinely available, which may not be for a decade or more.

Of course, it has been suggested (in Appendix I to HN(86)34) that two sites at least of the six taking part in the RM pilot projects will include the 'development and implementation of patient costing'. Certainly this is to be welcomed so long as it is clear that these projects are experimental, or of a research and developmental character, with the project outputs designed to provide doctors, nurses and other professionals increasingly with useful information for their decision-making, but with no pretence that patient costed management control budgets will become quickly available. The use of patient costed or case mix weighted management control budgets will need a great deal more research and development, over and above that required for Griffiths' CMBs. This is examined further in Chapter 9.

**8.19** HN(86)34 explains that the six sites chosen for RM pilots comprise a balanced mix of teaching and non-teaching hospitals, of hospitals at different stages of development of management information systems, and also a wide geographical spread. Aside from experiments in patient costing (with or without the inclusion of DRGs), what might these RM pilots attempt to include in their experiments – or indeed what might be included by other hospitals outside the pilot sites but eager to develop their own RM initiatives with the active co-operation of doctors and nurses?

This author would like to advocate an 'organic' approach. Organs are essential parts of a larger body or system. Organs can be studied and treated individually, although there is ultimate interdependence among them within the total system. Organic change or growth is assumed to be natural or spontaneous, and gradual. In contrast, CMB may be likened to a holistic approach, but recent experience appears to have demonstrated that we cannot yet apply the holistic approach effectively for lack of understanding (i.e. accurate data and costs) for the constituent parts, or what is here termed the organs. Of course, progress over the next decade may allow us to return to that approach, and to apply CMBs successfully and universally, later on in the 'nineties.

**8.20** For the purpose of this analogy the principal organs of patient care would be specified as including: wards, theatres, clinics, diagnostic services/laboratories, pharmacies, and paramedical services. If the principal objective in conducting RM projects is to reduce costs without reducing proper standards, so as to fund either an expansion of the volume of health care delivery or the redeployment of savings to priority services and other new developments, or both, then it might seem logical for RM projects to focus in particular on those organs which have the highest total cost and therefore the greatest potential for savings and redeployment of really useful sums.

Wards are the biggest and costliest organ. But the costs of clinical demands made on theatres, diagnostic services and pharmacies are also very large. Indeed, pharmacies are probably the organs where the highest proportion of cost is represented by variable cost, or the cost of consumables, and where cost reductions or savings can be made most quickly if found justifiable within the quality standards of clinical care.

**8.21** Suppose that one takes one or more of these organs to form the basis for a RM project. What should be the elements of the project? It is suggested here that each organ should be treated in three stages. Let us take radiology as an example.

In an earlier chapter it was illustrated how the 'functional budget' for radiology fails to include all the costs of providing the radiology service. So the first stage would be to study all the resource inputs of radiology, trace their costs, and reassign those costs from whatever other functional budgets to which they are currently charged, to the radiology cost and budget centre. One would then know for the first time what the total costs of the radiology service are.

It follows that the second stage should be to probe the reasonableness, or the why and wherefore, of all the main cost headings within radiology. In particular this would involve concern for the recharged costs which had previously been unseen only because they had been charged against other functional budget holders.

The third stage, with *all* costs of radiology identified, listed and checked, would be to recalculate new, true 'unit costs' of radiology services. Radiologists and consultants could then assess these unit costs in terms of the value or benefit of the various services: the consultants looking for tests which could be reduced in volume because of not really being needed (i.e. not giving good value for money), and the radiologists looking for savings from the reduced volume of tests, or from a better organization of service delivery.

**8.22** In any RM pilot projects which include cost inquiries such as the example in the preceding paragraph, the judgements of both consultants and department heads will probably be based mainly on experience, intuition or 'feel' for what is value for money relative to the likely benefit to patients. This is pioneering work. But as the years go by, with the development of case mix classification and costing, and more effective provision and use of comparative performance indicators, our capability to assess efficiency and value for money will improve, and will come increasingly to relate to established guidelines of good practice. Similarly, for nursing, it should become increasingly possible to plan (and to control cost against plan and budget) for more rational levels of nurse staffing, especially in wards.

**8.23** At least at the present state of the art, the main guidance on rational, or optimal, nurse staffing levels appears to derive from nursing dependency studies. This is a more objective approach than some former initiatives which involved experienced nurses making rather subjective estimates of the amount of nursing time patients in particular specialties should receive. This latter method almost invited, if in doubt, some overstatement of the volume of nursing needed.

Nurse staffing cost is, in the author's belief, the largest single element of NHS cost (the family practitioner services aside). Nursing pay is therefore the most important single source of expenditure to study, whether in RM projects or elsewhere, for possibilities of waste and for the potential of financial savings and redeployment. This extends to study of nurse absenteeism and training time, and not just paid nursing time in wards, theatres and clinics.

**8.24** Table 8.1 illustrates the kind of cost information which can be made available for wards. It is an output of a Griffiths CMB project, but any district with Körner specialty costing efficiently installed could probably produce similar information for use in a new RM project. The table is of course a summary, and supplementary reports would break down the detail

*Table 8.1 Budget variances ward report*

| | Current month Budget | Current month Actual | Current month Variance | Year to date Budget | Year to date Actual | Year to date Variance |
|---|---|---|---|---|---|---|
| | £ | £ | £ | £ | £ | £ |
| **Summary expenditure** | | | | | | |
| Nursing staff | 14,309 | 13,940 | -369 | 42,927 | 40,219 | -2,708 |
| Allocated expenses | 4,964 | 5,283 | 319 | 15,049 | 16,154 | 1,105 |
| Direct budget allocation | 19,273 | 19,223 | -50 | 57,976 | 56,373 | -1,603 |
| Apportioned overheads | 9,696 | 11,507 | 1,811 | 29,346 | 32,066 | 2,720 |
| Total expenditure | 28,969 | 30,730 | 1,761 | 87,322 | 88,439 | 1,117 |
| **Bed usage** | | | | | | |
| No. of available beds | 27 | 27 | | 27 | 27 | |
| No. of available bed days | 810 | 810 | | 2,457 | 2,457 | |
| No. of occupied bed days | 593 | 710 | 117 | 1,819 | 2,111 | 292 |
| Patients discharged | 95 | 110 | 15 | 285 | 303 | 18 |
| % bed occupancy | 73.2 | 87.7 | 14.5 | 74.0 | 85.9 | 11.9 |
| Average no. of unoccupied beds | 7 | 3 | -4 | 7 | 4 | -3 |
| Throughput per bed | 3.5 | 4.1 | 0.6 | 10.6 | 11.2 | 0.6 |
| Turnover interval | 2.30 | 0.90 | -1.40 | 2.23 | 1.14 | -1.09 |
| **Unit costs £** | | | | | | |
| Cost per available bed day | 35.76 | 37.94 | 2.18 | 35.54 | 36.00 | 0.46 |
| Cost per occupied bed day | 48.85 | 43.28 | -5.57 | 48.01 | 41.89 | -6.12 |

Source: Southmead Health Authority.

of nursing staff costs, allocated expenses, and apportioned overheads. (Incidentally, the apportionment of overheads conforms to Griffiths, but Körner does not recommend this in specialty costing, so such data may not be readily available in most districts).

Leaving aside the overheads (which presumably are fixed costs not likely to be affected by decisions on nurse staffing or ward use), it can be seen in this example that nearly three-fourths of the direct budget costs identifiable to the ward arise from nurse staffing costs. But the allocated expenses are also substantial, and as a large part of these presumably are consumables, they form an additional area for close study of cost efficiency additional to nurse staffing.

**8.25** Nursing dependency is an approach to measuring the volume and expertise (and volume × pay rate for expertise = cost) required for different patients. The UK work done on this to date is, in the author's belief, largely based on deriving a system for objectively classifying individual patients by reference to the data on their individual hospital records. Alternatively, in future, if all patients are routinely classified into DRG categories, it may be practicable to assign nursing dependency weights directly from the DRG status to which individual patients are assigned.

Conceptually, the structure of nursing dependency measurement is closely similar to the analysis of fixed and variable cost explained in Chapter 3. That is, every patient taken into a bed, even if ambulatory, requires a basic minimum of nursing time: this, if you like, is the fixed cost per occupied bed. Additionally there will be nursing care/time/cost rising like a variable cost function with the increasing dependency of patients who are more handicapped, aged, seriously ill or with multiple complications, etc. Intensive care units and special care baby units would presumably be at the top of the list in dependency weightings. Ideally, dependency should take account of the grade of nursing skill needed, and not just the volume of nursing time.

In the author's understanding much of the best of the early UK work on nursing dependency was done in Cheltenham, was then developed further in the FIP patient costing project at Coventry, and is now being field-tested and refined further at Cheltenham and a number of other districts. It is an essential development for rational planning of nurse training and nurse staffing, not to mention cost expenditure control. It is to be hoped that a number of the new RM pilot projects will include nursing dependency assessments within their protocols.

**8.26** Perhaps even more in community units than in acute units, the costs of the nursing and allied professions is the dominant cost, while the efficiency of the organization of their work is a crucial factor in both the volume and the quality of community health care delivery. The author doubts that the equivalent of nursing dependency studies is as yet so far advanced for community care as for hospitals, but nevertheless much useful information will become increasingly available. This will derive from the Körner requirements and the development work done on this at MIPP, the pioneering work on community activity and cost information done by FIP, and the apparently promising progress of the community MB demonstrations commissioned for the Griffiths programme.

Table 8.2 displays part of one type of report developed in one of the two first-generation community MB projects, at Worcester. This example is not a cost or budget report, but an analysis of workload. Its maximum utility to management will come about only after there is a run of a few years' data, to allow the plotting of trends and the study of seasonal variations, or when similar data from comparable districts is available to allow comparisons of relative volumes of service and productivity, after taking staffing levels into account.

The second reason for including this table is to demonstrate, should any readers of this book need such evidence, the degree to which the district nursing service is committed to the elderly. Table 8.2 shows workload for one month, subdivided by age bands. At least two-thirds of the workload is with clients aged over 75. The financial implications of this sort of evidence, given expected further rises in the numbers who live to age 75 and beyond, are alarming.

## Capital and revenue

**8.27** Up to this point this book has been almost entirely about NHS 'revenue' funds, which can be contrasted with what are termed 'capital' funds. Capital funds are provided to the NHS regions by the DHSS so that they, working with districts, can meet the major bills for hospital building, modernization, etc. The plant and equipment for new hospital premises is also paid for from capital funds, but most replacement plant and equipment has to be purchased from revenue funds. Revenue funds are the ongoing cash limit allocations to health authorities which are fairly constant (in real terms) from year to year, and which are used to meet the main NHS costs of payroll, consumables and other day-to-day operating expenses. Functional, specialty and Griffiths CMB costing and budgeting systems to date are concerned solely with expenditure from revenue funds.

**8.28** Up until now, the resources acquired from capital funds (e.g. land, buildings, plant and equipment for new buildings, and certain high-cost replacement equipment restricted to purchase only from capital funds in order to retain central policy control) have been 'free goods' (in economic jargon) so far as concerns district and unit managements, clinicians and other staff. They have been free goods in the sense that managers and clinicians have not had to pay anything out of their revenue budgets (i.e. their recurring income) to (a) acquire the assets, (b) repay the cost of the assets, or (c) meet the annual interest cost of the monetary value tied up in the assets.

This practice is commonplace in central government activities, but rare elsewhere. In both universities and local authorities, for example, the servicing of capital costs are required to be met from revenue funds – just as private individuals have to provide for the interest and repayment of principal on a loan to buy a car, as well as setting something aside, preferably, towards the cost of the next car when the present new car suffers its annual deterioration (or depreciation) from wear and tear or obsolescence.

Table 8.2   District nurses' activity count and time reporting

| Period from (1/7/86) to (31/7/86) Code description | Number | % | Tot time | % | Age bands 0-1 | 1-4 | 5-16 | 17-54 | 55-64 | 65-74 | 75-84 | 85+ |
|---|---|---|---|---|---|---|---|---|---|---|---|---|
| B7  Blood pressure | 27 | | 216 | | 0 | 0 | 0 | 4 | 2 | 4 | 13 | 4 |
| M6  Mid stream specimen of urine | 1 | | 12 | | 0 | 0 | 0 | 0 | 0 | 0 | 1 | 0 |
| S8  Specimen | 6 | | 78 | | 0 | 0 | 0 | 0 | 0 | 1 | 4 | 1 |
| SE  Swabs | 1 | | 9 | | 0 | 0 | 0 | 0 | 0 | 0 | 1 | 0 |
| U3  Urine testing | 145 | | 1,595 | | 0 | 0 | 0 | 2 | 12 | 24 | 96 | 11 |
| V2  Venepuncture | 11 | | 99 | | 0 | 0 | 0 | 1 | 1 | 3 | 6 | 0 |
| V4  Vital signs | 34 | | 180 | | 0 | 0 | 0 | 0 | 3 | 7 | 25 | 1 |
| W3  Weighing | 16 | | 48 | | 0 | 0 | 0 | 2 | 2 | 4 | 5 | 3 |
| Totals for: Taking samples & measurements | 241 | 1.41% | 2,237 | 0.90% | 0 | 0 | 0 | 9 | 20 | 43 | 151 | 20 |
| A4  Application/care of prosthesis | 13 | | 156 | | 0 | 0 | 0 | 0 | 0 | 4 | 9 | 0 |
| A5  Applic/removal bandages/aids | 1,175 | | 21,402 | | 0 | 0 | 2 | 83 | 56 | 188 | 636 | 224 |
| A6  Application of medicants | 489 | | 3,006 | | 0 | 0 | 2 | 33 | 41 | 78 | 219 | 128 |
| D3  Dressing | 1,941 | | 31,664 | | 1 | 0 | 8 | 342 | 178 | 415 | 736 | 299 |
| SD  Suture removal | 44 | | 704 | | 0 | 0 | 7 | 16 | 9 | 7 | 4 | 1 |
| W5  Wound irrigation | 90 | | 1,092 | | 0 | 0 | 0 | 25 | 42 | 2 | 21 | 1 |
| Totals for: Sutures, dressing & related pr. | 3,752 | 22.00% | 58,024 | 23.58% | 1 | 0 | 19 | 499 | 326 | 694 | 1,625 | 653 |
| CC  Collect & transport equip/supp | 248 | | 2,500 | | 0 | 0 | 1 | 42 | 12 | 53 | 77 | 65 |
| Totals for: Delivery of aids/equipment | 248 | 1.45% | 2,500 | 1.01% | 0 | 0 | 1 | 42 | 12 | 53 | 77 | 65 |
| CD  Collection of prescriptions | 92 | | 920 | | 0 | 0 | 0 | 9 | 3 | 19 | 36 | 25 |
| EC  Escort children to special scl | 5 | | 150 | | 0 | 0 | 0 | 0 | 0 | 0 | 0 | 5 |
| HF  Hospital visit to client | 8 | | 280 | | 0 | 0 | 0 | 0 | 0 | 1 | 5 | 2 |
| HC  Household tasks | 631 | | 8,242 | | 0 | 0 | 0 | 10 | 18 | 159 | 272 | 175 |
| PB  Preparation of food/drink | 176 | | 1,790 | | 0 | 0 | 0 | 2 | 27 | 59 | 69 | 22 |
| Totals for: Social help | 912 | 5.34% | 11,382 | 4.62% | 0 | 0 | 0 | 21 | 48 | 238 | 382 | 229 |

Source: Worcester & District Health Authority.

**8.29** In both economics and accountancy 'capital' is defined as investment or assets having a prolonged useful life, as distinct from, say, payroll costs which are 'gone today', or the purchase of consumables which will be 'gone tomorrow'. Indeed accountants have a very precise definition for capital assets – that is resources whose use or value in the organization will exceed one year – so that the fair assessment and charging of their costs will need to be spread over two or more years.

Thus in private businesses, most charities and many other parts of the public sector, annual revenue budgets are charged with the current year's share of the wear and tear, or deterioration or obsolescence costs, of the capital assets (or fixed assets) in use by each budget holder. This annual charge is termed 'depreciation'. No such charge is made in the NHS. And while the full cost of replacement of many worn-out NHS assets may in fact be paid for from the health authority's funds, this cost will not appear as an annual depreciation or 'asset use' charge in the current revenue budget of the department receiving and using the new equipment.

The argument here is not to imply that many departments in the NHS do not need new investment in more modern, reliable and productive capital equipment. Rather it is to assert that instead of the present situation, where capital spending often appears to result from who can shout loudest, protest most, or have the most influential contacts, we should in future have a more rational situation where budget holders will meet the capital costs of their equipment assets fully out of their revenue budgets, and where the allocation of capital spending (whether met from the capital allocations or the revenue allocations to the district) will depend upon objective assessments of need for, or savings from, the new capital investment outlay. It is harsh to have to meet the full capital costs of new equipment from a single year's budget, and it would provide a much fairer measure of annual operating costs if these could be spread, by depreciation charges, over the useful life of the new equipment.

**8.30** In the NHS, as in many other public bodies, objective assessments of need for capital spending are officially expected to be based upon 'investment appraisals', or 'option appraisals' as they are now usually described especially in the non-trading parts of the public sector. Investment appraisal is an analytical method of project evaluation which is used in the private sector and also in nationalized industries and some other public sector trading organizations. It seeks to predict the likely profit return on capital over future years, using discounted cash flow analysis (DCF) and attempting to allow for commercial/market risk.

It is a method of analysis which is not easily transferable to public services, such as the NHS, where all funding is intended to be spent and no profit or surplus is sought. To cope with these problems, option appraisals were devised for the public services. These involve a relatively disciplined study of the 'options' available to solve a specific problem. The study should assess the relative costs and benefits of each of the perceived options for solving the problem. If the problem is which combination of boiler capital costs plus fuel running costs is cheapest, the analysis will be relatively straightforward and based on purely financial criteria using DCF analysis as in the private sector.

**8.31** But if the problem is more complex, for example in deciding whether to build a new wing on a hospital overlooking a smoking steelworks, or whether to expand at an existing hospital on a congested inner-city site, it is obvious that there are decision factors which are difficult, and controversial, to quantify. It is in particular to deal with complex decision situations such as the above that the analytical approach of 'option appraisal' has been designed. The detail of option appraisal is beyond the coverage of this book, despite its importance. Interested readers should consult the Glossary.

**8.32** Setting aside the question of whether or not one should invest in long-life (fixed) assets in any particular case, the problem more relevant to this book is whether or not budget holders should receive a charge against their revenue budgets for the wear and tear, or erosion of value, of the plant and equipment for which they are responsible and which they are using in providing health care services. This issue has become of increasing importance both out of concern that the NHS is 'out of line' with normal financial accountability practice and therefore liable to come under increasing criticism, and also because of concern that departmental managers may be led into making wrong decisions (i.e. decisions involving total costs which are uneconomic relative to the health care and social benefits provided).

In addition, reviews and comparisons of performance between departments (or districts) may be distorted and misleading under the present situation. For example, take two laboratories in different hospitals but providing exactly the same range of diagnostic services. One may have the misfortune to be equipped with old fashioned, low productivity equipment, thus requiring a high and expensive level of staffing. The other laboratory may have been re-equipped recently with sophisticated, automated test equipment at high capital cost, but which enables high test productivity with low labour costs. Clearly it would be unfair to compare these two laboratories without including the annualized cost of the relative usage of capital, together with the current cost of labour and consumables already included routinely in NHS functional costing and budgeting for service departments.

**8.33** We can usefully subdivide the capital or fixed assets of the NHS between 'policy assets' and 'operational assets'. Policy assets are those for which accountability rests at a high level, e.g. with UGMs, the DGM or even the authority collectively. These assets would consist primarily of land, buildings and major plant installations such as heating systems. Operational assets comprise lesser plant, equipment (medical, laboratory or office) and vehicles.

Operational equipment is, or should be, bought primarily on the decisions and responsibility of individual service department heads, clinicians, nurses or administrators below UGM level. The costs of use, maintenance, wear and tear, and replacement of these operational assets should be included in the (revenue) budgets of the accountable managers. In recent years two important reports were published dealing with NHS management of these two categories of capital assets. Let us briefly consider their relevance.

**8.34** The Ceri Davies Report (*Underused and Surplus Property in the*

*National Health Service*) was published in November 1982. It was primarily concerned with the NHS's utilization of land and buildings (i.e. policy assets). Not surprisingly, the Report found that the NHS had been a rather complacent landlord. Awareness of the capital value or market value of property was limited, and little attention had been given to the opportunity costs, that is little firm planning had been done to predict the minimum amount of land and buildings likely to be needed for future developments, or what would be surplus and could be disposed of. This should not have been surprising, given that no rent or other charges were imposed on health authorities (other than maintenance and payments in lieu of rates where appropriate) for the Crown assets of land and buildings they held, and given also that if surplus land or buildings were sold, the districts involved were not normally entitled to retain and redeploy the capital receipts! Also until recently it had been the case that HAs were not legally able to apply for planning permission for the most profitable alternative uses of property (to maximize sale value), nor are HAs allowed to develop and operate or let their surplus premises for commercial purposes.

Finally, in paragraphs 5.26 and 5.27 of the Davies Report there were recommendations that 'notional rents' should be determined for NHS property, and that the volume of a district's property, as represented by its total of notional rent costs, should be taken account of in annual performance reviews. Districts which persisted in retaining excessive property might need to be given some financial penalty.

**8.35** The Report of the Capital and Asset Accounting Working Party (*Managing Capital Assets in the National Health Service*) was published in May 1985. This report was produced by the Association of Health Service Treasurers (now known as the Healthcare Financial Management Association) at the behest of the Körner Steering Group, to make good a gap of coverage in the Körner Sixth Report, on Finance. This CAAWP Report partly overlapped the Davies Report but it also ranged much wider, covering both policy assets and operational assets.

Being *de facto* a Körner Report, it gave considerable attention to the need for improved records, or asset registers, and the minimum data sets which should be collected on fixed assets. The Report also gave considerable attention to possible reforms in the way the DHSS enforces relatively arbitrary distinctions between capital funds and revenue funds, their uses, and the manner of accounting and reporting for them. (However, it is beyond the role of this book to consider these issues in detail.) Finally, the Report contained similar arguments to those in the above paragraphs to the effect that management information and control, and the usefulness of performance comparison information, would be improved in the NHS if the annualized costs of holding and using capital assets were to be included in budgets and cost reports. It proposed pilot trials to test three alternatives (paragraph 6.5.4) as follows:

— asset depreciation charges as used by the private sector;
— a system where RHAs would lease all major items of equipment, land and buildings to DHAs;
— a leasing system for land and buildings, and depreciation charges for equipment.

**8.36**   The pilot trials were intended to report by 1988, with the possibility that new capital assets costing and information systems could be introduced across the country from about 1989. Implementation might have to be spread over several years, as enormous work will need to be done to bring NHS asset records and registers up to a good standard, and many assets will need objective current valuations by independent experts.

As regards the three alternatives covered in the trials, this author believes that the third is the most promising. Land, by its nature, normally does not 'depreciate'. The cost of wear and tear, or loss of value, in buildings is very difficult to estimate, and it is confused by the amount of repair and modernization work that takes place. But it should prove feasible to develop a leasing system, or a 'fair rent', for each combination of land and buildings from year to year. These are the policy assets, for which it seems reasonable that the 'opportunity costs' of capital, or some near surrogate, should be used. Lease or rental charges would reflect market forces, recovery of capital value, and interest rates.

That would leave the operational assets (equipment and vehicles mainly) to be included in management budgets and cost reports on a depreciation charge basis. Operational assets are typically short-lived, but also essential in the short term. So the question of opportunity costs and market forces does not arise for them in the same way as for policy assets. Depreciation charges based on wear and tear and likely obsolescence represent a fair total charge to budget holders for their use of capital assets.

## Conclusions

**8.37**   The author hopes that some of the resource management (RM) experiments, pilots or related local initiatives will include work on the costs of using capital assets, and on their implications for budgets, decision-making and the optimal use of available resources. But of course the main expenditure of the NHS is on revenue costs, not capital costs. A natural instinct will be to conduct studies concentrating on the costs of consumables bought-in from outside the NHS – it always seems easier to cut spending on service from outside suppliers than on service from one's own employees. But the hard fact of life is that nearly 75 % of NHS revenue funds spending is on pay. The only way to make major savings on existing workload in order to help finance new developments or priority resource redeployment into the community health services, or to meet imposed funding cuts, is to reduce labour costs. The payroll costs of nursing is the most obvious target, which doubtless will be looked at closely in some RM projects. But major progress may have to await the full implementation of Körner, the general adoption of nursing dependency measurement, and also the general availability of case mix costing and budgeting discussed in the next chapter.

# Summary

1 HN(86)34 announced a change of policy in the speed and approach with which management budgeting for clinicians (i.e. CMB) should be developed throughout the acute services of the NHS. Instead of priority for CMB, emphasis should be given to the wider concept of 'resource management'.

2 The change of emphasis arose apparently because of disappointing progress in the districts pioneering CMB. The causes of this may include: delays in filling posts in the DHSS management board and for unit general managers; the time it takes to change organizational cultures to reflect the Griffiths recommendations; lack of time and skill devoted to interesting and motivating clinicians to take part in CMB; underestimation of the complexity of work to upgrade and computerize activity and workload 'feeder systems'; and shortage of sufficient senior staff to cope with all the above problems simultaneously.

3 HN(86)34 provides for 'new model' projects in resource management (RM) which should be undertaken only where doctors and nurses are actively involved in the management process. These projects should experiment in developing information systems which doctors and nurses find useful. The projects will continue at least through 1988 (though this author thinks some of them may need to continue to 1989 or 1990 for fair trial). The initial six projects have been approved by the Joint Consultants Committee, but their continued co-operation will be conditional on post-project evaluations confirming useful results.

4 Some of the new RM projects are expected to experiment with 'patient costing', and some may experiment with cost analyses of 'DRGs' or with 'case mix costing and budgeting'. These are all important clinical and management information systems for the future, and accordingly they are discussed in the next chapter. For the present, however, they are very much experimental initiatives, essentially of the nature of 'research' in the author's opinion. Ongoing, routine recording and reporting systems for patient, DRG or case mix costing or budgeting will require progress to information and computer sophistication even beyond the level which has caused problems for the CMB trials.

5 RM projects could usefully experiment additionally with ways of taking account of the costs of using capital – the estate, plus plant, equipment and vehicles. The annual costs of wear and tear of using capital assets should be charged to cost and budget centres. The Ceri Davies Report called attention to neglect of management costing and control of the estate, while the AHST report should result in information from trials to find if depreciation charges and/or notional asset leasing cost charges are feasible to calculate and to include in budget holders' budget allocations and costs.

# CHAPTER 9
# Patient costing and case mix budgeting

## Recapitulation

9.1 It may be helpful at this point to recapitulate how far we have travelled through the historical development and increasing sophistication of NHS financial and other management information. The progression is illustrated in Table 9.1. The first four chapters explained basic concepts of cost, costing and budgetary systems, and they also demonstrated how far – or not so far – NHS financial information systems had progressed prior to Körner, the 1982 reorganization to establish unit management, and the Griffiths initiative to establish 'general management' at every level. In mitigation, the DHSS had never before given much priority, let alone

Table 9.1    Progress of NHS financial information systems

| | |
|---|---|
| 1948 | Subjective costing based on hospitals and boards. |
| 1974 | Functional costing and budgeting based on management by function (i.e. profession) at district level. |
| 1982 | Functional costing and budgeting based on unit level management. |
| 1987–89 | Implementation of Körner reforms of NHS management information, including specialty costing. |
| 1983–89? | Experiments with clinical management budgeting (CMB), leading from late 1986 to wider ranging experiments in resource management (RM) for clinicians and nurses, sometimes including the developments listed below. |
| 199? | Development of patient costing information routinely available, based on FIP experiments from 1979 and with increased priority from the 1986 launch of RM projects. |
| 199? | Development of case mix (or 'workload') costing and budgeting combining information from patient costing with information on the case mix treated (e.g. information from diagnosis related groups (DRGs) analysis, perhaps eventually with adjustment (i.e. weighting) for case severity/complexity). |

resources, to developing NHS management information, and without the revolution in minicomputer and microcomputer data processing at low cost, rapid progress would anyway not have been possible.

As the Table summarizes, from the origin of the NHS up until 1982, only subjective cost classifications and district-centred functional costs and budgets (to reflect the 1974 reorganisation) were routinely available in the NHS, while information on activity/workload, use of manpower and use and cost of other resources (consumables, equipment, land and buildings) was almost uniformly poor outside a few isolated research experiments. What then became available to the unit management is explained in Chapter 5. But it must have been obvious to any concerned, proactive unit general manager that the information routinely available was not sufficient to assist the improvement of efficiency and effectiveness in an era when most districts and units were experiencing either absolute cuts in real resources or at least substantial cuts in their rate of growth in resources.

**9.2** So the first five chapters chronicle the state of the art in management information, or certainly in financial information for management, as regards information which should be routinely available at unit level and above throughout the NHS in England and Wales. The information in Scotland and Northern Ireland may differ slightly in detail and jargon, but essentially it is at the same stage of evolution. Meanwhile, starting before the Royal Commission Report of 1979 but accelerating thereafter, research and development projects to improve NHS management information proliferated. Körner, CASPE and FIP were the most notable of these, with Griffiths as a late addition. Körner was the first to provide definitive change which seemed quickly feasible and was accepted by the DHSS as the basis for mandatory reform of data collection and reporting for management control.

Körner information is distinguished through involving a balanced progression of activity/workload, manpower and financial information in parallel. The important financial information feature of Körner is the introduction of specialty costing as a routine and largely uniform system, a subject dealt with in Chapter 6. The first annual returns of specialty costs should be available in all districts by mid 1988 (for hospitals) and mid 1989 (for the community). This will be useful for performance review and comparative analysis. But some districts may not quickly meet Körner's desired standards in the accuracy of data recording (in preference to sampling), so it may not be unreasonable to think that the routine monthly (or even quarterly) reporting of specialty costs for local management use within units may not become universal before the early 1990s.

**9.3** The first five chapters explained what financial management information is, or should be, routinely available everywhere right now. Chapter 6 explained what should become routinely available everywhere within a year or two. Chapter 7 explained what Griffiths thought should be available generally within the NHS by, perhaps, the early 1990s. This was clinical budgeting, or clinical management budgeting (CMB), to reflect the concept that doctors are the source of demand on NHS resources and should be helped with information on the cost of their demands, as well as being held accountable for the cost relative to their workload.

But the Griffiths clinical management budgeting initiatives starting from 1983 did not progress well. The Griffiths Inquiry team and DHSS staff (this was in the days before the NHS Management Board had been appointed) seriously underestimated the amount of work and cost involved in leaping from functional costs and budgets all the way to clinical costs and budgets without first receiving and digesting the Körner reforms. Indeed, arguably even the Körner reforms to NHS management information will not prove sufficiently advanced, computerized or sophisticated as to support first-rate clinical budgeting.

In such circumstances, Griffiths clinical budgeting development sites had to devote most of their energy to development of the underlying information systems. Clinicians typically received little education in what to expect from CMB or how to use it. It appears that a rising number of them became suspicious that the new CMB system would become more useful to unit and district management in enforcing simple expenditure controls, and perhaps cuts, than they would prove useful to the clinicians themselves in studying and understanding their clinical workload, and how to treat that workload best with given resources. And for many clinicians there must have come a growing consciousness that the 'workload' itself was being measured by too simplistic criteria to be greatly helpful in studying their use of resources, or their comparative performance relative even to other clinicians in the same specialty.

**9.4**   Traditional workload indicators include number of patients seen, or discharged, number of occupied bed days, number of operations performed, and the like. These numbers, even within a given specialty, provide no clue to the differing health care needs of individual patients. They do not reflect differences in diagnostic status, in case severity or in clinical complications, such as are likely to vary in the case mix of individual clinicians from time to time, or to vary between the workload of individual clinicians over time because of differing special skills and interests, and thus the case mix referred to them. Chapter 8 reviewed problems encountered in the Griffiths CMB demonstration projects, and how these projects have come to be overshadowed by new model pilot projects in resource management (RM).

Unlike the central topics in earlier chapters, RM is not a specific type of financial information or analysis. Rather, it appears to be conceived as a series of projects or developments governed by a 'state of mind' of commitment to study of any and all obtainable information helpful to doctors, nurses and other health care professionals interested in making better use of available resources for patient care. Conceptually, this can be welcomed. And certainly it will be welcomed for additional funding resources to be made available to provide financial advisers, management consultants and other analysts to work at the elbow of the clinical professions to help them to study their use of resources, and to improve on this.

But this still begs the question of how far, in practice, it will become possible to classify and 'weight', in resource need terms, the workload of individual clinicians. Clearly at least some of the new resource management projects are intended to experiment in patient costing, and in analysis by DRGs (diagnosis related groups). These are important and promising developments – although too much progress should not be expected too quickly, lest there be disillusionment unnecessarily – and it is the purpose of this chapter to discuss these two developments, their potential, and their likely rate of progress.

## Patient costing

**9.5**  FIP (the Financial Information Project) began in 1979, funded jointly by the DHSS and the West Midlands RHA. It was funded as a research project and never given the scale of resources provided for the Körner and Griffiths initiatives. In hindsight this could appear to be unfortunate, as eventually it may turn out that patient costing has at least as much to offer to improved information and management as do those other, better known initiatives. Field research for the Royal Commission revealed widespread interest in obtaining information on patient costs (i.e. the costs of treating individual patients, or individual types/categories of patients). Similarly, the Körner Steering Group was brought under some pressure to include patient costing (PC) in its recommendations. But Körner was set up to determine what was quickly, routinely and universally feasible, and apparently it was felt (probably correctly) that the supporting data systems needed for accurate patient costing could not be made universally available in NHS districts within the Körner time-span for implementation of their recommendations (i.e. 1987–88).

**9.6**  It appears that the FIP was given an unusually wide brief, to firm up its detailed research activity only after a preliminary survey of what information users in the NHS felt to be desirable developments. Apparently the desire for patient costing information was the dominant response, as PC became the dominant and unifying theme of the FIP's work. This work developed through two projects in each of two approaches.

One approach was to test how far existing information, using micro- and minicomputers and financial modelling techniques, could produce reports useful in management planning and resource allocation. Two field trials were held. One trial used a microcomputer and a package spreadsheet program to demonstrate the feasibility of forecasting how a hospital's total costs would change as the age mix of patients and the relative demand on different specialties altered through time. The second trial, in Shropshire, used existing service planning information to demonstrate how a mini-computer could be used to output a costed planning model for the commissioning of a new district general hospital on a 'green field' site (with implications for likely contraction in the resources of other hospitals in the district).

**9.7**  In the author's view the above two trial projects were diversions down byways. The work was not unique. There have been a variety of other developments using computers in modelling information for planning (and for resource bargaining with RHAs), such as perhaps most notably the system developed in Bloomsbury. But these planning models rely on inputs of information derived from sampling and estimations. They do not claim or achieve a high degree of accuracy. They cannot be used for the month-by-month, year-by-year close analysis and monitoring of performance at the level of specialties and individual clinicians, which is the central theme of this book.

**9.8**   The second approach followed by the FIP probably will prove to have a more unique and enduring benefit to the NHS. This second approach involved developing ongoing, grass-roots level recording of the physical volume of services (manpower) and other resources (consumables and use of equipment etc.) used on behalf of the care of individual patients.

Again, two field trials were held, one in acute hospitals of a district (Coventry) and one in the community services (South Birmingham). Both of the field trials were successful in that they demonstrated the potential from their methods, but both were (limited) failures to the extent that they failed to achieve complete, comprehensive 'all-singing, all-dancing' patient information systems. The problem was the same as in the Griffiths demonstration trials – that is (as so often seems to be the case more generally in the UK, including in British industry) the scale of the work needed and the resources needed to accomplish the work were grossly underestimated. This is with benefit of hindsight yet again, but given the state of NHS patient data and related information systems in the early 1980s, producing patient costs was a feat roughly comparable to climbing Mount Everest without oxygen.

**9.9**   The field trial in acute hospitals was funded for two years and aimed to prove the feasibility of tracing costs through to individual patients in a small sample of specialties. However, even a single specialty can give rise to resource use and costs in nursing, medical, diagnostic, paramedical and other supporting services, including operating theatres. In the Coventry trial 27 different resource areas had to be studied, as regards validating or improving their activity/workload records, introducing or validating identification codings for individual patients, and establishing unit costs for the services provided.

This was a mammoth task, attempted before the Körner data improvements, specialty costing, or Griffiths CMB support (i.e. 'feeder') information systems had been introduced. It is not surprising that the final results from the original FIP acute hospital patient costing trial appeared to be 'patchy'. However, major progress was achieved in the areas of ward nursing and operating theatres, and for both of these areas the FIP team has subsequently developed standard systems available to any NHS health district, complete with instruction manuals and information on computerization.

**9.10**   Operating theatre costing is rather complex and problematic, both because of the variety of professions and consumables which may be used, and because of the pressure and occasional trauma of work which may make it difficult for nurse managers or other recorders to note, measure and record (manually or by direct entry to a computer terminal) the exact amounts of all staff time and other resources used. Operating theatres are one of the important 'facilities' whose costs were discussed in Chapters 6 and 7.

But of course ward nursing is usually more costly than the work in operating theatres, and generally it will be the most expensive single cost (and budget) centre in any hospital. Thus, accurate and relevant activity and resource use measurement is of the highest importance for wards and their impact on costs and budgets, even in acute units which have not yet gone forward to detailed specialty costing, clinical budgeting or patient costing. The FIP systems can help in this.

**9.11** Facilities costing for ward nursing is simpler than for operating theatres. This is because the pay costs of only one discipline, nursing, are usually involved. Also consumables are a minor portion of cost compared to pay, and the recording of use of both consumables and nursing time can be done in a much more deliberate (and therefore presumably more accurate) way than in operating theatres. And so, if we have accurate recording of time and consumables, and if all we want is ward costs for control, or ward costs plus budgets for planning and control, then there should be no problems.

But if we are going forward to patient costing, or even only to specialty or clinical costing or budgeting, then there will be problems. The problems arise because different types of patients make differing levels of demand on the volume and the quality of nursing services, so that 'average costs per day' for an occupied bed in a ward will have little credibility when recharged to separate specialties, firms, individual clinicians or patient groupings whose cost reports, and/or budgets, will be heavily influenced by the precise amount of the recharges. There is therefore a need to be able to measure the amount of nursing care (and its cost) provided to individual patients.

However, to attempt to identify the precise amount of nursing care, and the grade (i.e. cost) of nurses involved, for each patient separately, as an individual, would be time-wasting and probably fraught with error. To cope with this problem, the notion of 'nursing dependency' has been developed, and the FIP has made an important contribution to nursing dependency information systems which will be helpful to patient costing (*and* to specialty costing or clinical budgeting).

*Nursing dependency*

**9.12** The concept of 'nursing dependency' is simple. Individual patients need unique and varying amounts and types (and therefore costs) of nursing care. The basic minimum of nursing care (and time and thus cost) is defined by the ambulatory patient ready for discharge from hospital. From that minimum one progresses to the patient ambulatory only with nursing assistance, to the patient fully bedridden. Other criteria also arise, such as the frequency of checks (e.g. of pulse or temperature) or tests, the frequency of medication, etc.

From nursing experience and nursing records it is quite practicable to derive measures of relative demand on nursing resources – provided of course, that nursing records are accurately and consistently maintained. Pioneering work in measuring nursing dependency was done in

Cheltenham, as well as in other NHS districts and overseas. The Cheltenham work was developed further by the FIP in the Coventry trial – and now this FIP system is being tested and developed further back in Cheltenham and other health districts.

Of course ideally nursing dependency information is a 'spin off' (or derivative) of an information system primarily designed to assist managers (in this case, nurses) to optimize the beneficial use of the resources at their disposal. Nursing managers will seek to make sure that they staff their wards to the levels indicated by nursing dependency. Unit general managers and their financial advisers will seek to monitor that, on average, the levels of nurse staffing and grading (and costs), do not exceed the levels of nursing need indicated by the reports of nursing dependency they receive. Thus nursing dependency systems can provide an immediate control information benefit to unit management, additional to their contributions to patient costing studies and monitoring.

**9.13** The other FIP trial was the project to develop better information for management in the community services. This covered home nursing, loan of equipment, domiciliary incontinence service and geriatric health visiting in the community. Standard (computerized) data collection and information systems are now available from FIP (see Glossary) to cover most of these areas. Taken together with the development work of MIPP (see Glossary) there is now a strong foundation for management information systems in community health care – and presumably this will be incorporated into some of the new RM projects following on from the pioneering work of Bromley and Worcester (and MIPP, at Bromsgrove and Redditch).

**9.14** The 'FIP's Information Systems Philosophy' was published in *Public Finance & Accountancy* (10 January 1986). The four main points were that management for monitoring, etc., should be a 'spin-off from information for day-to-day management'; that information systems need to be 'part of the operational work of the department'; that 'activity, manpower and finance should be brought together in *one system*'; and that 'systems should be *patient-based*'.

All four of these points, or objectives, seem consistent with the Körner initiatives, even if the immediate practicability of the last two objectives cited seemed so unrealistic that Körner perhaps felt obliged to give little emphasis to them. But indeed the FIP team in practice accepted the latter argument, and in the above article they concluded:

> Attempting too much is a mistake. It is not reasonable to expect to provide satisfactory information systems in all areas at once. The national initiatives, though using simplistic activity data, still require the development of relatively complex systems. Systems should be developed in the priority order required by each district, linking each system as necessary through the patient identifier (the unique patient number used in all Patient Administration System initiatives). . .

Expressed differently, and by analogy, it seems to the author that the FIP team, like other researchers, came to appreciate that NHS management information is like a giant system of interlocking cogwheels. It is unreasonable to expect that all of the inefficient or inadequate cogwheels can be replaced in one 'Big Bang'. The information subsystem represented by each cogwheel can be researched, analysed and redesigned to a higher standard, and then, when ready and tested, it can be substituted in place of the degraded, or worn out, cogwheel in the present information system.

**9.15** The above quotations from the FIP refer to the 'patient identifier' or the 'unique patient number'. The unique patient identifier number is essential in patient costing. That is, it is essential that each patient has an identifying number which is not, and cannot be, shared or confused with any other patient. This is necessary so that all those direct costs of treatment of each patient get recorded and charged to that patient, and not to any other patient by mistake. In other words the 'identifier number' is a code to instruct the computer to which account (or in this case, which patient) costs should be charged (or recorded).

Coding of cost has always been needed in the NHS, or at least since control accounts came to be computerized at regional level many years ago. From 1974 expenditure costs had to be coded for charge against the accountable district level functional officer. From 1982 this coding had to be amended to identify the accountable unit level functional officer.

Proper specialty costing/budgeting or clinician costing/budgeting similarly would require coding (accurately applied) to the level of the specialty or consultant accountable for calls upon pharmacy, diagnostic services, theatre time and ward time, etc. And if the identity coding is carried down to the level of the individual patient, then one has the ultimate 'building block' for aggregated cost analysis. That is, assuming that the patient identifier code is accompanied by a second code number identifying the consultant responsible for that patient, it becomes possible to produce cost performance information for (a) the patient, (b) groupings of patients, (c) the consultant, (d) the clinical firm, (e) specialties, (f) clinical divisions, and (g) the clinical services of the unit as a whole.

**9.16** The collection of costs (and the setting of budgets against which cost performance can be compared) for levels (c) through (g) in the preceding paragraph is of course perfectly feasible without need for the unique patient identifier (although the latter would provide a crosscheck on the correctness of cost charging). We have discussed costing and budgeting at these levels in preceding chapters. As regards (a), costs expended at the level of the individual patient, this information may not be required as a routine reporting output: doctors properly do not think in terms of cost averages, or limits, when treating individual patients. However, consultants might on occasion wish to see the cost details for individual patients, either for review of the apparent cost effectiveness of their patient management profiles, or else as part of the data input to a more formalized medical audit.

Even so, the interest in patient costs is likely to be the greater, and the more useful, when it is information on (b) groupings of patients which is routinely reported and reviewed. Groupings of patients is of interest where there are common characteristics: these could be age, sex, marital status, race, degree of social deprivation or whatever (depending upon reliable information for classification being available from the records). But the most likely grouping of patients, certainly from the point of view of studying resource use and cost effectiveness, presumably will usually be a grouping based on similar medical conditions, or similar diagnostic status. This latter classification is reviewed in the next section of this chapter, under the heading of 'diagnosis related groups' (DRGs).

**9.17** Some readers may be surprised to learn that the NHS does not already operate patient costing systems, assuming that private hospitals have for many years had such systems as the basis for charging their private patients. There are two aspects to answering this implicit query.

First, private hospitals do not charge their patients the precise 'cost' of their individual treatments. Rather they charge patients a 'price' for their treatments: this can be an 'all in' price or more usually an itemized bill containing the prices of services and resources utilized. Prices typically are set more on the basis of what the market (i.e. patients and insurers) will pay, bearing in mind the prices of competitors, than on the basis of cost. Some prices might even be 'loss leaders' as in corner shops or supermarkets, to promote interest and new customers. Bear it in mind that the legitimate objective of all commerical enterprises – within the quality standards imposed by themselves, by the marketplace or by independent regulatory authorities – is simply to maximize profits, i.e. the excess of *total* income over *total* costs. So, at least until recently, the distinctive aspect of financial control in private hospitals appears not to have been concern for the accurate costing of a total episode of inpatient care, but rather a concern for rigorous scrutiny of the costs of individual 'cost centres', such as nursing, pharmacy, catering, etc.

But secondly, the same dramatic reductions in the cost of computing which have been essential to cost and management information systems developments in the NHS have also enabled private hospitals to instal systems monitoring and analysing their costs in greater detail. This is especially the case in the USA, where an increasing proportion of health care funded by governmental and other insurers is paid for at prices pre-determined by the funding body rather than by the hospital. So, American hospitals must look more closely at their costs in detail, to verify that their costs are less than their prospective reimbursement. This pressure on American hospitals to monitor patient costs, and to contain or reduce costs, is a major consequence of the introduction of DRGs.

## Diagnosis related groups

**9.18** Diagnosis related groups (DRGs) is a method of classifying acute care patients according to their diagnostic status. This method has been developed over a long period of research and development led by Professors Thompson and Fetter of Yale University. There are 467 separate, defined categories in the DRG classification system, plus a 468th category for cases which defy classification. This American system of patient classification has been adopted widely in Europe and Australasia for the study of needs and trends in patients care, and sometimes also to provide a basis for costing and charging for patient care services.

In the UK the use of DRGs is still only at the stage of research, but there is a very lively interest. CASPE Research, at the King's Fund College in London, provides a clearing-house service for the exchange of information on the several British projects testing the use of DRGs for the NHS. It also produces the *Diagnosis Related Groups Newsletter*, published three times a year.

The DRG classification for individual patients is made from the information entered on patient records. In the UK this classification is based on data in the HAA records. Whilst admitting that there is much doubt regarding the accuracy of HAA records, they are probably broadly accurate in the majority of cases. Their active use for costing, resource allocation or other managerial uses would probably generate successful pressure for a higher standard of accuracy. The relevant HAA data on patients is held on computer file at RHAs, and this can be accessed for DRG analysis using DHSS software first developed by Dr Hugh Sanderson. It is understood that DRG analysis will play some part in one or more of the new model resource management pilot trials. So therefore we need to consider the relevance of DRGs to financial information and control in the NHS.

**9.19** DRGs specify standardized, uniformly defined, units of workload for *acute* hospital services (note to date they are not reliable measures of health care workload for psychiatric, geriatric or other long-stay or community care services). It follows that these standardized DRG outputs should provide information useful for costing and budgeting in the NHS. Although hospital doctors properly should retain full discretion for deciding how to use available resources in the treatment of individual patients, it is nevertheless the case that over a period of time when many similar cases are treated, say a year, some pattern of typical or average resource use and costs will emerge. From this evidence one may derive a 'standard cost' of treatment.

Alternatively, or additionally, one may discuss with consultants to establish, for each DRG in their field, what resources they would expect to need – including medical, nursing and paramedical staff time, diagnostic tests, drugs, theatre time (where relevant) and estimated LOS. These estimates of resource needs can then be costed, item by item, to provide an alternative specification of the standard cost of treating an 'average' patient in any specified DRG category.

Then, after analysing the past year's case load by DRGs, and after adjusting for any estimates of altered circumstances or policy initiatives to deal with waiting lists, etc., it should be possible to derive a rational and realistic budget for the workload of each clinician. Hence the terms 'costed workload' and 'workload budget'.

**9.20** An important criticism frequently made of the DRG classification approach is that it fails to discriminate between relatively easy and relatively difficult or complex cases, i.e. the 'case severity' factor. This will apply especially to patients treated by centres of regional specialties, and departments in teaching hospitals more generally, where it tends to be assumed that the case mix contains an above average proportion of complex or advanced cases.

Indeed, in the USA where the DRG system was developed, and where costed DRGs are used as the basis for reimbursing hospitals for patients treated under the Medicare programme for the elderly (and increasingly DRG reimbursement rates are being used also for state Medicaid programmes and for charging private health insurance schemes), it has been recognized that average DRG costs (and reimbursement rates) are insufficient to cover the legitimate total costs of teaching hospitals, so that supplemental funding is required. Of course in the UK we already have supplemental funding for teaching hospitals in the form of SIFT (Service Increment for Teaching), but it is contentious how far SIFT adequately finances the extra cost of the high standards and high technology care expected in teaching hospitals.

**9.21** There has been much research, especially in the USA, into methods of objectively assessing 'case severity'. Measures of case severity could then be used as a weighting factor to adjust 'DRG standard cost' to indicate realistic cost targets for the actual case mix of patients treated in any give hospital. However, the research results to date appear to be inconclusive and controversial, in that no system has yet been devised for grading case severity which has been demonstrated to be free of significant error or the risk of subjective bias in use. Therefore it is not realistic at the present point in time to do more than to note the problem, and the need for further research here in the UK, until we can obtain firm evidence regarding the relative resource requirements of patients with differing degrees of case severity and complications (and thus of resource needs and costs).

## Flexibility in budgeting and resource allocation

### Flexed budgets

**9.22** The introduction of 'flexed budgets', or flexible budgets, was one of the innovations considered in at least two of the original CMB demonstration districts. Flexible budgets are budgets which expand or contract with changes in the volume of workload dealt with by the budget holder. Such budgets are widely used in the production, selling and distribution functions of industrial companies, where prompt response to changing market conditions is essential.

In contrast the NHS normally uses only 'fixed budgets', where budget holders' allocations are predetermined at the start of the financial year (as a fixed portion of the total cash limited funding allocation of the authority). Fixed budgets make it easier to control total spending within the cash limits, and this eases the risk exposure (and adrenalin level) of health authority chairmen, general managers and treasurers. Introducing flexible budgets into the NHS would increase the risk exposure of possible overspending, but this could be recompensed several times over by the release of energy of those consultants who want to increase output and shorten waiting lists.

**9.23** Flexible budgeting may not be immediately practicable in most health districts where functional budgets remain the order of the day. It is consultants who effectively control the volume of throughput of the hospital and until they take up the role of principal budget holders, whether individually or as team members of a firm, specialty or division, flexed budgets may not be feasible because, to avoid chaos, control over the use of resources must be matched by precise accountability. Also flexible budgeting is not feasible without accurate knowledge of the breakdown of expenditure/costs between fixed and variable (i.e. primarily consumables). The true fixed costs (mainly the pay of permanent staff) must remain 'fixed' (or constant) in the budget, but the variable costs of drugs, dressings, prostheses, X-rays and tests, and even catering, etc., can be allowed for as a marginal element of budget to be added to, or deducted from, allowed budget in direct proportion to the extra patients treated, or the shortfall, as compared to the workload target originally set at the beginning of the year.

If all consultants responded to the use of flexible budgeting by markedly increasing admissions and throughput, then obviously the health authority would be in difficulty with its overall budget. But this seems an unlikely scenario, and even if it did happen, efficient monitoring by the treasurer should detect the warning signs in time to ring the alarm bells and enforce a slowdown on admissions. The accuracy of the monitoring of the costs of admission and treatment will be the greater, once DRG classification of patients is standard practice in the NHS, and once the expected 'standard costs' for each DRG category have been estimated and can be used in acute hospital budget allocations.

## Virement

**9.24** Virement is the transfer of allocated or budgeted funding from one budget to another, or from one budget heading or subheading to another. Many districts have elaborate rules and regulations governing the rights of virement by budget holding managers (see Chapters 4 and 5). And clearly, where large sums of money are involved and the virement is between different major functions or units, then close scrutiny by district management or the authority is required.

But arguably the NHS is counter-productively bureaucratic in the extent to which individual managers (including clinical budget managers) are restricted in their rights to vire resources. Clearly budget elements which relate to fixed costs such as the pay of permanent staff, cannot be altered in the short term. But as regards expenditure on consumables, equipment, etc., this author believes that maximum flexibility of choice and decision-making (and thus of rights of virement) should be allowed to budget holders in the NHS, provided of course that they remain within their global budget limits.

## Recharging

**9.25** Recharging (sometimes called 'cross charging') involves the transfer of financial accountability from one unit to another, one district to another, or even one region to another. In effect it is the selling of services between two different parts of the same organizational entity at an agreed price. Budget allocation, or actual cash, changes hands. Recharging also occurs in the private sector, for example between the divisions of large industrial companies such as ICI.

Recharging has not been a frequent or important feature of NHS financial arrangements until recently, aside from situations such as where a district operated a large laundry and provided a regular service, on a cost-sharing basis, to another neighbouring district. Recharging did not arise in patient care services because of the NHS tradition of referred patients being allowed or even welcomed to cross district and regional boundaries whenever this appeared to be in the best interest of patients, as judged by GPs and hospital consultants. But with tight resources, there are growing pressures to restrict the mobility of patients across district boundaries. As we shall see in the final chapter, the use of recharging whereby cash follows where patients go for treatment, may be one way of maintaining flexibility in the distribution of patient services, while at the same time protecting patient (and GP) freedoms to seek hospital care wherever this will be in the best interest of individual patients.

## Summary

1 Health care resource needs, and thus inherent costliness, varies between individual patients, between patients in similar groups of health status classification, between individual clinicians (whose case mixes may vary widely within the same specialty), and thus between hospitals and even districts. The causes of variation in need and costliness include differences in diagnoses, severity, complications or complexity, age, social deprivation, etc., of patients. They also include differences between doctors in their chosen methods of treatment, the technology available, and the 'intensity' with which doctors use available resources.

2 Existing NHS activity and financial information systems cannot be used to compare performance between different departments or individuals in the same specialty, because these systems are incapable of classifying patients and reporting their resource consumption subdivided by most of the above factors that lead to differing levels of resource need and cost. Even with Körner specialty costing or Griffiths CMB in full use, the classification of patients will still be inadequate to allow fair performance comparisons based on the data routinely available.

3 New developments in NHS information will rectify most of the above deficiencies once research and experiments are complete, and once adequate financial resources and managerial (and clinical) support are put behind their full implementation into operational systems. Some of the resource management (RM) projects may make a very useful contribution to this progress.

4 The new developments which should help are patient costing, where all resource uses are coded to the individual patient and can be charged (notionally) to him or her, and DRGs (diagnosis related groups) which is a system for classifying patients into groups with similar diagnoses plus similar resource cost requirements. In future it should become practicable to combine these two systems into one integrated 'case mix costing and budgeting' system, with outputs subdivided by specialty, individual clinician, or patient group.

5 Work on DRGs is in hand at several places, including CASPE. Patient costing has been pioneered by FIP (the Financial Information Project), notably in the areas of ward costing and nursing dependency, theatre costing, and community services resource management and costing. But much work remains to be done before these two types of systems become fully developed.

6 A further development needed in future is greater flexibility and equity in the provision of resources in response to work done, and in charging one part of the NHS for services rendered to its service population by another part of the NHS. These aspects of flexibility and equity can be assisted by wider use of flexed budgets, virement, and recharging for services rendered between units and districts.

# CHAPTER 10
# What the future offers

**10.1** It is not possible to predict the future accurately and in detail, although perhaps a few broad, generalized predictions not likely to prove wrong could be attempted:

a   Real resources and the financial resources which make them possible will continue to be, and certainly will appear to be, in short supply relative to the demand, and need, for health care services. This is due primarily to the ageing population, rising expectations and the continuing development of high-tech (and high cost) medicine. The degree of shortfall in resources may vary from government to government, but whatever any government's complexion and priorities may be, there always will be too many demands on the public purse for the NHS ever to receive as much resources as its staff believe it could usefully deploy.

b   In the above conditions of apparent resource shortages, it is inevitable that there will continue to be strong and perhaps even growing public, political and managerial pressure upon NHS doctors, managers and other professionals to demonstrate their productivity, efficiency and effectiveness in the use of resources. The measurement and monitoring of resource use, activity/workload and output is bound to increase in volume and sophistication almost regardless of the degree of co-operation of the members of the professions being monitored.

c   The use of computers to record and analyse resource use and workload will increase inexorably as the cost of computing continues to decline and skill in using computers builds up. This will increase the speed and accuracy by which senior managers can measure, monitor and challenge the performance of clinical and all other staff.

d   It is a continuing trend in our society generally (i.e. not just or particularly in the NHS) that the traditional authority of professions to set and self-regulate their own standards is being whittled away. This trend is visible in the universities, accountancy, the City, the civil service, and so on. NHS professionals cannot escape this trend. Increasingly society, through the DHSS, through health authorities (which at some future date may be elected bodies, presumably with increased influence), and through general managers, will seek to specify priorities, workloads and standards of quality of output and service.

This is a development largely independent of (a), (b) and (c) above, but it will be intensified by them.

The foregoing predictions provide the main background assumptions governing this author's arguments and forecasts in this, the final chapter. The chapter subdivides into two sections. In the first section we look at the next few years, concentrating on the prospects for implementation of the financial information reforms already launched or planned. The second section looks further ahead to what changes could occur, and perhaps should occur, in the final years of this century.

## Implementation of financial information developments

*Körner*

10.2 Körner management control minimum data sets, data recording and reporting requirements started into universal use in the hospital service from April 1987, and will start in the community services from April 1988. Thus in theory much of the implementation of Körner should already be complete. Staff should have been trained. Data capture arrangements, data entry forms and procedures, and new computerization where funds allow, should by now have been introduced throughout the hospital services sector.

Doubts exist, however – at this stage on purely anecdotal evidence – that the above aspects of implementing Körner have so far been achieved in most health districts. Much more effort may be needed. Moreover, in some districts there appears to be resistance to putting great effort into making Körner data inputs and information outputs a great success. Sometimes this may be because of shortage of expertise and support resources at a time when other new information systems developments are occurring also.

Or is this at times an excuse? It may be that in some districts delay is largely caused by the doubts of particular managerial and other professional groups regarding the adequacy of information based on the Körner minimum data sets for meeting local management needs. It is difficult to get to the bottom of this. It must be a truism that many or even most of the Körner recommendations were to some extent based on compromises between competing interest groups, or between what was seen as desirable versus what was quickly feasible.

10.3 Overall, however, the Körner management information innovations must be seen as a watershed for rationalization of data sets and derivative information and reports useful in operational management control in the NHS. There will be teething problems, but in the author's opinion the overall concept and structure of the Körner reforms will within a few years become both generally accepted and conscientiously carried out. But this need not rule out the 'renegotiation' of individual minimum data sets where the potential for improving the value of the information output can be demonstrated. Also, it is only reasonable to expect that once the computerization of activity and other feeder systems has been more widely developed in all districts, there will be a good case for a sequel to Körner – a further major review of NHS managerial and professional information needs, and the standardized data collection requirements to meet these needs.

**10.4** Most of the Körner recommendations were concerned with the improvement of data sets or reports already in use. But the Körner initiative of most concern to this book, the introduction of specialty costing, was entirely new research arising from experiments and developmental trials, as discussed in Chapter 6. Average costs per specialty should become available for inter-district comparisons and analysis within districts, from mid 1988. At this stage it is not possible to forecast how far the specialty cost figures for the early years will be reliable for comparison purposes, given variability in the quality of the underlying activity feeder systems, and possibly in the application of cost allocation methods used to weight the activity measures to build up the total cost for each specialty.

However, it is the author's belief that even imperfect specialty costs will be found so interesting and useful for managerial studies and performance evaluation that there will be continuing pressure to improve the feeder systems and accounting processes to the point where much more accurate figures are routinely provided, probably increasingly on a monthly reporting basis to unit managers and to interested consultants. Of course this will still leave unanswered the problem of variation in the case mix between nominally the same specialties located in different hospitals/districts. The answer for this will have to await the development of operational systems of patient costing.

### Griffiths

**10.5** As a result of the Griffiths Inquiry, development of clinical management budgeting (CMB) began in four acute units in 1983, and subsequently at least twenty further districts have begun CMB systems development (see Chapters 7 and 8). Progress has been slow, both because of the inadequacy of the supporting feeder systems for resource use and patient activity, and because resources to interest, educate and involve clinicians have been inadequate in most districts.

It is difficult to forecast how soon, and to what extent, hospital consultants will willingly take on the role of clinical budget holders for the total resources used in the care of their patients. Consultants certainly need improved orientation or education about CMB, but probably more critically they need to be convinced that the information on which their budgets, and the costs charged to those budgets, are based is both accurate and relevant. Of course, as feeder activity and costing information systems continue to improve in many districts, treasurers will be able to supply unit general managers with analyses of the costs charged against the workload of individual clinicians, even where the latter are not holding budgets.

So, in a sense, clinicians who do not take part in CMB are forfeiting an opportunity to participate in forward planning of the resources and workload on which their performance is anyway sooner or later going to be monitored. Once effective specialty costing is operational, all that is required to make costing effective to the level of the individual clinician is the addition of an accurate identifier code to all transactions which traces to the accountable consultant either directly, or indirectly through identification with each patient treated.

**10.6** Resource management (RM) started pilot trials from late in 1986. It is too early to assess progress, but the principles of RM appear sound. The essence of these principles appears to be that new NHS management information systems should be tailored to meet the information needs perceived by doctors and nurses. The pilot trials are experiments which, hopefully, will prove helpful to clinicians, nurses and other managers within the local unit. What is not clear is whether or not they will generate progress forward on uniform, routine reporting systems such as the NHS needs for generalizable guidelines on efficient and effective resource use, and for performance monitoring and reviews. In any event the new RM trials will not have progressed far enough for firm evaluation before 1988, and in the author's view definitive evaluation could well be delayed until something more like 1990.

This possible delay is because at least some of the RM trials are intended to include patient costing and DRGs (diagnosis related groups). Both patient costing and the linkage of costs with DRGs (see Chapter 9) are still only at the experimental stage in the NHS. So, presumably, the RM trials will need to expend much time on systems development, or mark time until systems are developed in other projects, or else conduct limited 'research type' projects in which data is extracted manually supported by much sampling and estimation rather as occurred in the trials of the Magee specialty costing system some years ago. Even the latter approach could provide useful evidence of the feasibility of involving doctors and nurses in responsible (financial) resource management, but there would still remain years of work in developing and installing economical, routine information systems capable of providing the same range of information on a routine basis to all clinicians and senior nurses throughout the NHS.

*CASPE and FIP*

**10.7** CASPE and FIP (Chapter 9) arguably are the two financial and management information projects which have come closest to meeting the needs of the future. That is said with the benefit of hindsight, as is the suggestion that it is a pity these two projects were not earlier given much stronger financial backing, so as to push the frontiers of NHS information forward much faster. It was CASPE which first spotted the importance of bringing doctors and nurses voluntarily into team co-operation in financial (resource) planning and control. Unfortunately CASPE's early projects were not always noticeably successful, perhaps partly because the supporting feeder activity and costing information systems were not good enough at the time, and partly because sometimes too few hospital consultants were willing to take part in this important innovation.

**10.8** FIP has pioneered the information systems needed to support patient costing (as needed in the new RM projects in acute hospitals, as well as in management budgeting projects in the community). However, even after several years' work, the operational FIP systems cover perhaps only about half of the total accountable cost related to clinical management. Perhaps the most important FIP work has been the development of workload measurement and costing systems for operating theatres and wards, with nursing dependency weighting systems additionally for the latter. Patient costing of course requires the very accurate identification (by the constant recording of the correct patient identifier code) of every unit of every type of resource used by each individual patient. We are some years away from having routine systems which permit comprehensive patient costing in every district.

10.9    CASPE and other UK researchers have been developing and testing the feasibility of using DRG classification systems on acute patients in Britain. To provide DRG classifications routinely is likely to require extra effort to ensure the accuracy and timeliness of the existing hospital activity analysis (HAA) data. This should not take long to achieve, once a practical need and priority are announced. DRGs are important because it is only by classifying the diagnoses (and probable treatment patterns and resource requirements) of patients that we can hope to compare the relative total resource requirements of individual clinicians, individual specialties, and the DRG-adjusted specialty mix of individual hospitals.

10.10    If the new resource management projects generate enthusiasm for patient costing, and if this in turn releases resources to expedite and complete the patient costing information systems, then it appears feasible that both patient costing and DRG patient weightings could be available by the early 1990s. However, since patient costing requires some considerable upgrading of activity and resource-use feeder systems above the standard required to meet Körner specialty costing standards, it could be up to ten years before such systems became universal throughout the NHS. The author forecasts that they will come to be required universally in the NHS.

But of course DRG workload costs and budgets are not the end of the road of systems innovation. DRGs do not adequately cover psychiatric, long-stay or community care, nor do they adequately reflect variations in case severity or complexity within individual DRG categories. Such variations will be important for resource allocation and costing for regional special-ties, teaching hospitals and other centres of excellence.

*Other developments*

10.11    There have of course been many research or systems development projects in the NHS in recent years, in the areas of concern of this book. In this chapter have been mentioned only the four which so far appear to have had the greatest impact: Körner, Griffiths, CASPE and FIP. A few other important initiatives have been mentioned in earlier chapters (such as MIPP, of special importance to community financial information and management systems), and a few further projects are identified in the Glossary. The only other development which should be mentioned here is the need for improved education and training of staff at all levels to cope with the new age of detailed cost information, budgets and performance indicators and reviews.

This improvement extends to junior staffing levels, where the need is for training in the importance of scrupulous accuracy in the capture and entry of data on all patient activity and resource utilization. To be effective this training must convey awareness of how the data will be aggregated and used later to help determine the future distribution, use and control of unit resources in the interest of maximizing the delivery of patient care from available resources. The need for improved education and training extends through all the professions providing senior staff and budget holders in the NHS, arguably including also clinicians even when they are (not yet at least) budget holders. In the case of clinicians, the sea-change to their education and attitudes should begin in the medical schools.

Of course similar comments have been made for years, with little visible impact as yet. However, rather like repeated seasons of frost eventually splitting a rock, it can be forecast that increasing attention will come to be given to the basic education of medical students and doctors in training in a basic understanding of health economics, management principles and the use of financial information. More detailed understanding can come later – basically what is needed is an opening of minds and a change in attitudes.

**10.12**  It is of course the task of the NHSTA (the National Health Service Training Authority) to give leadership and direction to the training of NHS staff, especially staff whose role in partly or mainly managerial. To the author, it appears that the NHSTA is caught between the hammer and the anvil. The hammer is the DHSS, with its priorities (via the NHS Management Board); the anvil is the operational NHS, with seemingly conflicting priorities and expectations between regions and districts, and the institutions representing individual NHS professions. The NHSTA has the author's sympathy, but its future performance must be of a high standard if the pace of progress not just to the existence of better management information systems, but also and more importantly to their active and effective use, is to be maintained.

*Comment*

**10.13**  Obviously if new financial and related management information systems are to be introduced quickly and effectively, there must be a large investment in staff training. Putting aside the question of whether or not the investment in staff training (at all levels) will be either adequately funded or sharply enough focused on practical needs, there is the further problem that trained 'workers' are wasted if not provided with good quality 'tools' of the type they have been trained to use. The tools in this case are computers, their 'software', their output to terminals or in 'hard copy', and the additional specialist staff needed to run these systems, interpret the output of data, and advise managers and clinicians on how to use the output as effective information for planning resource use and taking decisions (e.g. on admissions mix, ward nursing levels, best use of theatres, numbers of tests, etc.).

In this matter the DHSS is to some extent hoist on its own petard. For years it has been preaching the gospel of cutting back on management costs. It now realizes, in the author's opinion, that it is necessary to spend a penny in order to save two pennies for use in increasing throughput, or for redistribution to priority services and new developments. The question is: can and will the DHSS – in the face of pressing demands for the release of extra funds for immediate increases in the volume of patient care services – find the will to provide the extra funds needed to equip the NHS with better, cost effective information systems right now? Otherwise the impact will be diluted and achievement of the systems improvements already possible may drift into the 1990s.

## A longer-term view

10.14 Taking a very long view, with historical perspective and an awareness that cultural and societal preferences change both gradually and with occasional radical shifts (e.g. as with the coming of the Welfare State and the founding of the NHS in its present form), it is unrealistic to think that the NHS will continue in its present organizational framework into the indefinite future. Such speculation may at first seem outside the framework of this book, but we must remember that financial arrangements and information systems have no value in their own right – they exist legitimately only to reflect, monitor and serve the needs of the organization structure, funding arrangements and accountability requirements of human enterprises as they alter through time. And even in the next ten years, or by the end of the century, there is still the possibility of major changes in the organization and financial arrangements of the NHS (or, more generally, of the systems of health care delivery in the UK).

It is possible to foresee four possible scenarios for the year 2000, as follows:

a    The NHS continues broadly as it exists now. For historical reasons the NHS is an unusual, perhaps almost anarchic, mixture of centralization (e.g. funding plus guidance on priorities and on many matters of detail, including financial reporting) and of decentralization (e.g. local departures or delay in implementing national priorities, local accounting systems which do not conform to national standard systems, etc.). The present RAWP system of funding allocations aims broadly over a period of years to equalize the volume of health care resources within each district. With low total growth in funding, the RAWP equalization objective can be achieved only by cutting the funding of some districts (notably inner-city and teaching districts) for redistribution to other districts. Even so, nearly all districts feel financially constrained and there is some evidence of rising pressure within the NHS to restrict non-emergency services to local residents. This could reduce consumer choice and GP-referral choice, and also reduce competition to provide high quality care. Recharging for hospital services (see below) offers one possible solution to this dilemma. Patient costing and costed DRGs (Chapter 9) will provide equitable pricing information for setting recharge rates.

b    The NHS will become more centralized. It is possible that some future government might lose patience with the existing arrangements and, if it thought it had public opinion behind it, it might tackle head on the vested interests of clinicians, senior managers and others in the present system of diffused control and accountability. Regional health authorities might be downgraded to little more than regional outposts of the NHS Management Board and the DHSS, serving mainly as a clearing house for distributing standardized systems and information, and monitoring compliance and performance. Certainly no other very large organization, such as a big bank, high street chain or nationalized industry, would tolerate the diversity of workload and management accounting information systems and computer systems in use or being developed within the NHS.

c  The NHS becomes more decentralized, or truly regionalized. The present 14 NHS regions in England are too small to be efficient self-contained health services in their own right. But should England move to genuine regional self-government, or if the regions were reduced in number to four or five, and with elected authority memberships, then it could be feasible to have genuine decentralization of policy-making, priority-setting, and the development and control of funding practices and distinctive management and financial information systems. Any loss of economy of scale from the present mixture of central and regional guidance and limited standardization could be more than made up by the release of regional initiative, and by the opportunity for competition among the regions to demonstrate the best way forward in providing better service and better value for money.

d  The NHS might be partly or wholly dissolved. The primary principle underpinning the NHS is that the State should pay most of the cost of health care of the people, and indeed that it should pay all the cost of care for those least able to pay – the handicapped, the poor and the elderly. A secondary principle is that the State itself should own, staff and operate the facilities for delivering the health care it pays for (family practitioner services aside). The primary principle would not necessarily suffer if the secondary principle were abandoned. The government would simply pay other health care providers the allowed costs of planned, contracted or actual volumes of health care delivered. In this scenario, public and community health services might remain in a scaled-down NHS, or they might be relocated with local or regional government. NHS acute hospitals would be broken up, possibly with the option to bid to take them over open equally to local authorities, non-profit trusts and private hospital managements. A condition of having a license to operate hospital services could be the acceptance of very precise, standardized cost and workload measurement and reporting systems. In these, patient costing and costed DRG workloads would play a very important part in determining equitable prices (i.e. recharges) which the public purse would accept and reimburse. Indeed, under all four of the scenarios here briefly described, the whole range of contemporary financial information developments should prove useful, or even essential, in promoting good service delivery combined with value for money.

**10.15** The four scenarios above were included to demonstrate that improved financial information (with improved supporting feeder systems) is important regardless of the organizational arrangements from time to time, and indeed that the very viability of some organizational arrangements may depend upon accurate specialty costing, patient costing and the linkage of these to workload monitoring (and budgeting) based on DRGs. This same improvement in financial information could prove equally important if the organizational arrangements of the NHS were left essentially unchanged but the funding arrangements were altered. In (a) above there was brief mention of the difficulties being caused (especially in the four Thames regions) by the attempt to implement RAWP redistribution under conditions of virtually static funding (in real terms) recently experienced in several regions. These and other problems with RAWP have been recognized recently in a major Report by the NHS Management Board. This Report was looking mainly for improvements in the working of RAWP which could be implemented quickly, but it also encouraged further research on various matters, including the costs and funding of cross-boundary flows of patients and also the alternative of 'cross-charging' (i.e. what has been termed 'recharging' in this book).

**10.16** Regarding cross-boundary flow adjustments, the above Report suggests that some shortening of the time-lag in funding for these could be adopted as soon as Körner specialty costing and related information is routinely available. It suggests in addition that when case mix costing (i.e. patient costing combined with DRGs and preferably case severity analysis) becomes available further consideration should be given to reviewing the adequacy of the present costs (i.e. DHSS regression specialty costs), especially in the context of teaching hospital costs. Patient costs or case mix costs will not be routinely available in the NHS before at least the mid 1990s, but for the purpose of RAWP sufficiently accurate figures could probably be obtained by using adjusted average costs obtained from RM pilot trial districts.

**10.17** Adjustments to RAWP for cross-boundary flows of inpatients are currently made two years in arrears. Receiving some extra funds two years, or even one year, after providing a service by encouraging the admission of a patient from another district to fill spare capacity is not a strong incentive to managers or clinicians who will have to find the resources and the cash to treat that patient right now. An alternative, discussed in the above Report under the heading of 'An Internal Market?', is to allow districts to do deals with other Districts on planned flows of patients between districts, with cash (based on agreed costs) moving between districts with the patients. The 'agreed costs' could be either full costs or marginal costs (see Chapter 3). In either case, at present the costs will be 'estimated', as until patient costing or case mix costing is operational in the NHS perhaps several years from now, no costs for treating individual types of patients will be available at a more specific level than the Körner average specialty costs collected by districts.

**10.18** The advantage of the above cross-charged 'deals' between districts is that they could help to equalize supply and demand between districts, to improve equality of access, and to maximize the total volume of health care delivery. For example, district A may have spare capacity in orthopaedics.

District B may have a long waiting list for hip replacements, no spare capacity for operations but some spare non-recurrent cash. If the two districts can strike a bargain on a cross-charging price which is somewhere between marginal cost and full cost, both districts benefit. District B works off part of its waiting list at a reasonable price. District A earns more cash than its extra out-of-pocket costs (the marginal costs) to carry out the treatments.

**10.19** The other side of the coin to districts doing deals to increase patient movement inwards where cash quickly follows, is the risk of districts with funding problems seeking to discourage the inflow of patients not financed through 'deals', on the (probably unspoken) grounds that without extra cash they really cannot afford to treat such patients. Should this become 'acceptable behaviour' and spread, then we risk acquiring in the NHS the equivalent of the 'neighbourhood school', or the ghetto mentality (i.e. people trapped within confined boundaries). On the one hand this would reduce the choice of patients, sometimes for travel convenience, and it would reduce the choice of GPs, sometimes because they think their patients would benefit from a particular skill, or shorter waiting list, to be found in another district. And on the other hand, any restriction of patient movement across boundaries, and thus the creation of 'captive' patient populations, reduces the pressure of competition on districts to maximize the satisfaction (i.e. quality of care and of service) which they render to patients and their GPs.

**10.20** To counteract the above (i.e. the 'cross-boundary discouragement problem'), and also to approach as closely as practicable to a free market situation, we could amend the RAWP system by abandoning all cross-boundary flow adjustments (although there might have to be some special adjustments for regional specialties and teaching hospitals). Instead, districts would be funded under RAWP solely for their weighted resident populations. But every patient and GP would retain the right of access to any hospital, in any district, providing spare capacity and the relevant skills are available. The 'standard cost' (or adjusted average cost of treating that type of patient) would then automatically be charged against the RAWP funding allocation of the district of residence. The author would argue that this would be fair, would maximize consumer choice, and would maximize the pressure on hospitals to be efficient, effective in quality of care, and also welcoming to consumer (i.e. patient) preferences and environmental needs.

At present it would be difficult to operate such an 'open market' reimbursement system equitably, because the only costs available to use for reimbursement for patient flows between districts are DHSS or, shortly, Körner specialty costs. Specialty costs, as we have seen, do not adequately and fairly differentiate the costs of varying case mixes within individual specialties which can lead to quite different levels of cost per case. Case mix costing (i.e. patient costs classified by DRGs, and ideally by some severity weighting factor as well) can ensure adequate and fair reimbursement. Average case mix costs might be used as a standard recharging (or cross-charging) rate of payment between districts, but each district would need up-to-date case mix costs for its own treatment programmes in order to validate its performance and if necessary improve efficiency to ensure it was not 'losing money'.

With commitment and funding for good systems development, the financial information to support this internal 'free market' approach to NHS funding and costing could be in general use by the mid 1990s, or certainly well before the year 2000. We need to think well ahead: experience suggests it takes between five and ten years in the NHS to take-any new research finding forward through development, trials, validation, and making the funds and trained staff available to achieve routine, universal operation of any major new information system.

## Concluding comments

**10.21**   This book has sought to explain the nature and uses, and the strengths and weaknesses, of financial and related information systems developed in the NHS – in the past, present and future. Over the past eight years or so there has been an enormous investment of time and money in research and development of better activity, workload, manpower, patient administration and financial information systems within the NHS. To date little benefit or payoff has been visible from this investment to most people who work and serve in the NHS. The Körner reforms, and especially Körner specialty costing, will provide the first visible, major evidence of change and progress in the quality of NHS information for management.

It will be a few more years before there is much more visible evidence. Clinical budgeting may spread gradually, but it is not the ultimate management information and control system. For that we have to look further ahead, to patient costing related to diagnostic states (DRGs), and also adjusted for case severity and complexity factors once reliable weighting systems have been proven. This latter stage of improved information will not become routinely available in the NHS before at least the mid 1990s, in the author's opinion. Meanwhile, there is no excuse for clinicians, nurses and other managers not getting on with the job of making good use of the new Körner information, and of the gradual introduction of new supporting systems such as ward and theatre costing, new manpower control information, etc.

**10.22**   This text has not had space to describe even all those relevant research and development projects known to the author (and there must be many local projects which have gone unpublicized). Also the book has not been able to do full justice to financial and other management information developments for the community services. This is partly because notable developments in the community have been fewer and started later, partly because the author is less expert on community services relative to hospital services, and partly because it is anticipated that there will be a separate volume in this new series of NHS management books, which will be devoted entirely to financial and related management information developments for the community services.

**10.23**  Finally, the author hopes that readers will share with him an expectation that there is light at the end of the tunnel. For years the NHS has operated with inadequate information for planning, managing and controlling the use of its human and physical resources. Financial information systems of course are only a means to an end. They are one means towards the end of improving the quantity and quality of health care delivery within the available resources.

## Summary

1 The auguries for the future are that there will be rising need for health care as the population ages, and that there will be an even faster rise in the demands for health care as technology advances and public expectations expand. Given the economic forecasts for the UK, it seems unlikely that public spending on the NHS will keep pace with the need or certainly demand, regardless of what party is in power. Thus the pressure on NHS resources, and stress for its staff, are likely to increase. This can be ameliorated to some degree if resources are used to their utmost efficiency. Better financial and other management information systems can assist in this, if staff will make positive use of the information.

2 There will be a continuing erosion of the mystique of all professions, and a corresponding increase in the challenge to their autonomy, their judgement, and their use of resources. At the same time, the progress of computer and systems technology, at decreasing cost (in real terms), will mean that the resource use and workload of clinicians and other professional staff in the NHS (and in all other public and private sector organizations) will come to be increasingly closely monitored and challenged, regardless of the degree of co-operation of the staff concerned. But the more that staff participate, the more they will be able to influence the use of resources and the criteria by which their performance is judged.

3 The Körner reforms of management information will be implemented, though the author suspects often only gradually and grudgingly. But in time their value will be recognized, especially the innovation of specialty costing. Clinical management costing will follow next, with or without the consent of the health professions. Hopefully, with their consent this will be converted into clinical management budgeting (CMB). Next may follow patient costing, weighted by DRG information. That in turn should lead to case mix costing and budgeting, including the active use of recharging between and among all budget, unit, district and regional budget centres.

4 The successful implementation of the reforms of resource use and resource control which the NHS needs, will require expanded training of staff at all grades, and also the inclusion of study of health management, health accounting and health economics in the professional syllabi of all health professions.

5 By the end of the century the NHS could be drastically altered by greater centralization, by decentralization or regionalization, or by privatization (which includes dispersal to the control of local authorities or charities). If the risk of such changes is to be minimized, the onus lies on clinicians, managers and all other staff of the NHS to demonstrate that their efficiency and effectiveness in health care is of the highest standard.

# Glossary with Bibliography

This Glossary is intended to complement the ten chapters of the book. Equally it is meant to be useful as a self-contained reference source, even for readers who have not read the ten chapters. The Glossary is extensively cross-referenced, using both of the terms 'see' and 'q.v.'. The majority of Glossary entries are definitional and need no bibliographical source referencing. The other Glossary entries have bibliographical references of major relevance printed at the end of each entry.

There are a few books or reports of particular importance or wide relevance as regards the development of NHS financial information and control – these are listed first immediately below. That list is followed by a short list of the key journals which regularly report news and/or research on NHS financial resource allocation, budgeting, costing, activity and work-load measurement, and other related information systems and themes relevant to this book.

## Books and reports

Bevan G., Copeman H., Perrin J. and Rosser R. (1980). *Health Care: Priorities and Management*. Croom Helm, Beckenham.

Brooks Ray (ed.) (1986). *Management Budgeting in the NHS*. Health Services Manpower Review, University of Keele.

DHSS (1985 and 1986). Circulars on Management Budgeting and Resource Management, HN(85)3 and HN(86)34. DHSS.

Griffiths R. (1983). *NHS Management Inquiry Report*. DHSS.

Hillman R. (1984). *Specialty Costing in the National Health Service*. AHST/CIPFA.

Jones T. and Prowle M. (1987). *Health Service Finance* 3rd edn. Certified Accountants Educational Trust.

Körner E. (Chairman, Steering Group on Health Services Information) (1984). Sixth Report, *A Report on the Collection and Use of Financial Information in the NHS*. DHSS.

Levitt R. and Wall A. (1984). *The Reorganised National Health Service* 3rd edn. Croom Helm, Beckenham.

Perrin J. (1986). The National Health Service. In *Public Sector Accounting*

*and Financial Control* 2nd edn. edited by Sir Douglas Henley et al. Van
  Nostrand Reinhold (UK), Wokingham.
Royal Commission on the NHS (1978). *Management of Financial Resources
  in the National Health Service*. Research Paper No. 2, HMSO.
Wickings I. (ed.) (1983). *Effective Unit Management*. King Edward's
  Hospital Fund for London.


## Journals

*The British Journal of Healthcare Computing* (alternate months)
*Financial Accountability & Management* (quarterly, Basil Blackwell)
*Health Care UK* (annual, Policy Journals)
*The Health Service Journal* (weekly)
*Hospital & Health Services Review* (bi-monthly)
*Journal of Management in Medicine* (Henry Stewart Publications)
*Public Administration* (quarterly, Blackwell for RIPA)
*Public Finance & Accountancy* (weekly, CIPFA)
*Public Money* (quarterly, CIPFA and Public Finance Foundation)


## Glossary

**Accountability.** Whereas 'responsibility' is a generalized obligation of
managers and other professional persons to conduct their work in a manner
consistent with agreed objectives, the authority granted to them, and the
resources available, 'accountability' is more specific. It is the obligation to
render account or report on one's performance, involving the keeping and
disclosure of accurate records of work done and resources used. In the NHS
accountability to the DHSS and Parliament has always been present since
1948, naturally. More recently there has being growing interest in accountability, or at least wide disclosure of performance information, to the local
communities served by the NHS.

Association of Health Service Treasurers (1982) *Local Accountability*.
  CIPFA.

**Accounting.** 'Accounting' is the discipline and methodology of properly
recording and interpreting financial transactions, and of measuring,
recording and reporting the use of resources by organizations and their
individual managers. These resources include manpower, consumables and
capital assets, the use of each of which must first be measured in workload
units and then converted to units of expenditure or cost for aggregation and
analysis in the common denominator of monetary value.
  'Accountancy' defines the profession trained to practise 'accounting' and
to 'audit' (i.e. check or validate) the work of other accountants. (See
'Accountability' and 'Audit'.) In the NHS accounting work is done to meet
the professional standards advised by the Chartered Institute of Public
Finance & Accountancy, and the financial information recording and
reporting requirements set by the DHSS. The latter were revised recently to

take account of the reforms (e.g. specialty costing (q.v.)) following from the Sixth Report of Körner (q.v.).

DHSS (October 1986). *NHS Manual for Accounts*, DHSS, London.

**Accrual accounting.** 'Accrual accounting' is the method of accounting used in industry and commerce. It attempts to measure the true costs of resources consumed in producing the output of an organization over a year or other time period, unlike cash accounting (q.v.) which simply measures the receipt and use of cash, regardless of the level of workload. The NHS uses cash accounting and also income and expenditure accounting (q.v.).

**Actual costs.** 'Actual costs' is an everyday term for which accountants sometimes substitute the term 'historical costs'. This is normally understood to mean the actual monetary purchase price or expenditure to acquire particular consumables or other assets (see 'Asset accounting'). Practical problems can arise. Take the example of X-ray film. This may be bought in batches, at different times and at different prices. The 'different prices' may be caused by changes in the price of silver as a commodity, changes in the value of sterling relative to the dollar and other currencies, or by monetary inflation. Parts of different batches of X-ray film may be in the stockroom simultaneously, and often it may be pure random chance which item of film is taken out of stock on a particular day for a particular X-ray.

The link between actual cost in expenditure or acquisition, and actual cost of specific resources at the time of consumption thus becomes extremely tenuous. In response to this problem accountants may seek to charge budget holders with an 'average' price per unit of resource consumed with the latest price paid (i.e. more or less the 'replacement cost' of the consumable/asset), or with a predetermined estimated target average price termed the standard cost (q.v.).

**AHST.** See 'Association of Health Service Treasurers'.

**Allocation.** In accounting 'allocation' is the process of tracing accountability for incurring costs or expenditure to the cost centre (q.v.) or budget holder responsible. See 'Apportionment', 'Direct costs', 'Indirect costs' and 'Overheads'.

**Apportionment.** In accounting 'apportionment' is the process of estimating the share of cost attributable to particular cost centres or budget holders on some reasonable basis. This applies where cost accountability cannot feasibly be traced to individual user managers, as in the case of indirect costs and overheads (q.v.). For example, heating costs might be apportioned to departments on the basis of square footage of space occupied (regardless of heat source and insulation differences), or patient catering costs might be apportioned among wards on the basis of occupied bed days (regardless of menu variations).

**Asset accounting.** Assets are things or objects with qualities of usefulness or value. 'Current assets' are short-life resources like provisions, drugs and dressings; the NHS includes these in its cash accounts and expenditure accounts. 'Fixed assets' are long-life resources which do not get 'consumed' at one point in time, but instead tend to wear out or become obsolete gradually. Examples are equipment, vehicles and buildings.

Most NHS fixed assets are financed out of 'capital' funding allocations and the costs of their gradual consumption do not have to be charged to operating budgets funded from 'revenue' allocations. The result is that NHS units and budget holders do not get charged with the wear-and-tear and obsolescence of the fixed assets they use. This means that operating costs are understated in reports of functional costs, specialty costs, clinical costs and patient costs. These costs are less useful for performance comparison purposes.

The Körner programme was aware of this problem and asked the AHST Working Party on Capital and Asset Accounting to report on this and make recommendations. They recommended trials of fixed asset accounting using depreciation (q.v.), and also using notional rental or lease-charge costs. Asset accounting, including charges to budget holders for their use and accountability for fixed assets, could come into general use in the NHS by the early to mid 1990s.

AHST Capital and Asset Accounting Working Party (May 1985). *Managing Capital Assets in the National Health Service.* CIPFA, London.

**Association of Health Service Treasurers.** The 'Association of Health Service Treasurers' (AHST) was the specialist professional group for NHS finance officers. Under that name it contributed to the Körner Finance and other Reports, and especially to a study on managing NHS capital assets (q.v.). It is linked with the Chartered Institute of Public Finance and Accountancy (CIPFA) and was recently renamed as the Healthcare Financial Management Association.

**Audit.** 'Audit' or auditing is the process of checking and validating the accuracy and integrity of the financial practices, records and reports of an organization. In the case of the NHS, as in other bodies primarily financed from public funds, there is a particular audit concern to verify that money has been spent on those purposes, and only those purposes, approved by Parliament when voting funds. However, the scope of audits has widened in recent years so that, additional to financial probity, much time is now spent checking on economy, efficiency and the effectiveness of progressing agreed policy objectives.

NHS audit is at three levels: internal audit conducted by local audit staff on an ongoing year-round basis; DHSS annual audit conducted by DHSS auditors or by firms of chartered accountants on a subcontracting basis; and periodic audit by the National Audit Office (i.e. the auditors directly accountable to Parliament). See 'Internal audit', 'Salmon Report' and 'VFM'.

**Budgets/budgeting/budgetary control.** 'Budgets' are plans formulated as monetary authorizations of allowable cost or expenditure. These plans should include agreed targets of workload or output as well. This does not always happen in the NHS at present, but in future it should become a routine aspect of clinical budgeting (q.v.), case mix budgeting (q.v.) or other forms of management budgeting (q.v.).

'Budgeting' is simply the process of preparing budgets, preferably following a rational sequence of dialogue with management in which desired workloads/outputs are balanced with the costs of resources/inputs which management realistically can make available.

Once the financial year begins, costs or expenditure against authorized budgets has to be monitored, preferably monthly and with little delay, so that budget holders can know how well they are performing relative to their budgets – and so that general managers and health authorities will have the information they need to ensure compliance with funding allocations and to impose discipline on clinicians or department heads who occasionally seeks to consume more than their share of the available resources. This process is known as 'budgetary control'. To be fair, and effective, it requires adequate staffing by trained unit financial advisers or management accountants, with time to trace and analyse the causes of departure between budget plans and budget performance.

**Capital and capital assets.** 'Capital' has several meanings. To economists it means the 'real resources' used in an enterprise. To accountants it means both the monetary cost or value of 'real resources' and also the source of funding or ownership of the financial or monetary resources of the organization. The DHSS funds the NHS regions (and they allocate to districts) with two separate allocations. The bigger allocation is revenue (q.v.) for annual operating costs, including the replacement of most kinds of worn out existing equipment. The smaller allocation is capital, which finances new hospitals and hospital enlargements, new clinics, new service facilities, and the replacement of certain categories of equipment for which policy control or encouragement is desired to be retained at DHSS or regional level.

'Capital assets', usually called 'fixed assets' by accountants, are the 'real resources' comprised of land, buildings, plant, equipment and vehicles (see 'Asset accounting'). NHS capital assets comprising land and buildings are often termed the estate (q.v.) and these pose management problems rather different from those of industrial-type assets which wear out or become obsolete more quickly, i.e. plant, equipment and vehicles (see 'depreciation').

AHST Capital and Asset Accounting Working Party (May 1985). *Managing Capital Assets in the National Health Service.* CIPFA, London.
Cook A. (November 1983). *Capital Expenditure Control in Health Authorities.* South Western RHA and University of Bath School of Management.

**Carry-forward.** 'Carry-forward' is the facility for taking forward into the next financial year allocated funds which were not spent in the preceding year. The DHSS allows districts to carry forward up to 1% of unspent revenue funding, and up to 10% of unspent capital funding. The higher allowance for capital funding is because weather and other contractual problems make it difficult to regulate capital spending to precise timetables.

District carry-forward is normally used to help 'balance the books' from year to year, or else to ease the financing of new developments expected in the next year. Districts do not usually extend any budget carry-forward rights to their own internal budget holders, although strong units or even individual budget holders with good cases or good argumentative skills may at times be able to negotiate carry-forward on a grace-and-favour basis. See 'Virement', an arrangement to assist the strategic balancing of revenue (q.v.) and capital (q.v.) funds, especially when combined with the use of the carry-forward facility.

**Case mix costing and budgeting.** Case mix information systems involve the recording of information about patients which will allow them to be classi-fied by diagnostic characteristics, treatments and sometimes indicators of case severity or complexity. Each classification of patients, usually utilizing the DRG (q.v.) system, will tend to have a distinctive average cost or standard cost (q.v.) for treatment. Profiles of the normal workload of specialties or of individual clinicians can be constructed, costed and used as the basis for case mix costing and budgeting systems to plan hospital expenditure and review performance between hospitals. These systems will probably become the most important financial control instrument in hospitals, but they are not likely to be in use universally in the NHS before at least the mid 1990s. See 'DRGs', 'Patient costing' and 'Workload budgeting and resource allocation'. See also 'Resource management', the latest initiative of the NHS Management Board to encourage clinical involvement in management budgeting (q.v.), for which case mix costing and budgeting may be developed in some trial projects.

**Cash accounting/budgets/limits.** For purposes of UK government financial control the NHS is treated as an extension of the DHSS, that is it is financed and controlled on the same basis as the Civil Service and other central government services. This basis is 'cash funding' (subdivided between 'revenue' funds and 'capital' funds). The NHS is allocated a specified amount of cash to spend in a given financial year and must not spend more than that limit. This allocation is called the 'cash limit'.

In order to monitor compliance with this limit each health authority needs an overall 'cash budget' and a 'cash accounting' system to trace and balance cash expenditure against cash income. But while it is usually practicable for the authority as a whole to 'balance out' in cash terms, because of the large volume of transactions and possibility of, for example, expediting or delaying the cash payment of bills, replicating the same arrangement in the budget accounts of functional, departmental, facility or clinical budget holders would only cause confusion. Therefore for internal management budgeting and costing health authorities normally use income and expenditure accounting (q.v.).

Financial control to the government cash limit sometimes proves diffi-cult, especially because the cash limit is determined before the beginning of the financial year and may not allow fully for the amount of pay increases negotiated by NHS staff. Then, in order to balance the cash accounts, it becomes necessary to freeze staff vacancies, delay maintenance or equipment replacement, etc., leading to at least temporary cuts in the real terms (q.v.) volume of NHS resources available for patient care.

**CASPE.** See 'Clinical Accountability Service Planning and Evaluation'.

**Ceri Davies Report.** This report dealt with the management of the NHS estate (q.v.) and also with issues affecting asset accounting (q.v.).

DHSS (Chairman: Ceri Davies) (1983). *Underused* & *Surplus Property in the National Health Service*, London.

**Clinical Accountability, Service Planning and Evaluation (CASPE).** The CASPE Research Unit under the direction of Dr Iden Wickings was established in May 1979, linked with the King Edward's Hospital Fund in London and mainly funded by the DHSS. CASPE has pioneered the involvement of clinicians (sometimes with nursing and other disciplines) in financial planning and budgeting projects, notably through the system of planning agreements with clinical teams (PACTs).

The most notable recent developments have been projects at Lewisham and North Southwark Health Authority (Guy's Hospital), and at Brighton HA where a management budgeting system is being introduced and will be linked to a quality assurance programme, with quality of care in clinical terms monitored by means of voluntary peer review. CASPE also has become involved in research on DRGs (q.v.), running a user group, organizing seminars and producing the *Diagnosis Related Groups Newsletter*, and improving information for the management of the NHS estate, its capital assets (q.v.).

CASPE has produced over fifty articles, working papers and book contributions. Space does not allow a comprehensive list here, so interested readers should write to CASPE Research, King Edward's Hospital Fund, 14 Palace Court, Bayswater, London W2 4HT, requesting the latest edition of the CASPE booklet listing activities and publications.

**Clinical audit.** See 'Medical audit'.

**Clinical budgeting and costing.** 'Clinical budgeting' is a system where resource use and patient care workload planning are based on the clinician as controller of admissions and of decisions on the volume of diagnostic tests, drugs, etc., i.e. variable costs (q.v.). The plans are converted into financial budgets and are then monitored for performance compared to plan. Budgets cannot be monitored unless there is an accurate, directly related costing system capable of reporting promptly. See 'Griffiths Inquiry Report', 'Management budgeting'. 'User budgets' and 'Workload budgeting and resource allocation'.

Wickings I., Coles J., Flux R. and Howard L. (1983). Review of clinical budgeting and costing experiments. *British Medical Journal* **286**.

**Commitment accounting.** A system of accounting in which budget holders are charged with the exact (or, if necessary, the estimated) cost of resources ordered for purchase or consumption, without waiting for physical delivery and the supply of final invoices or cost sheets. It is a method of monitoring against overspending, and thus reducing financial risk. It also provides helpful information to budget holders to alert them against possible overspends. However, extra clerical and computer systems are required, and research for the Royal Commission a few years ago indicated that formal 'commitment accounting' is little used in the NHS, although apparently many functional and departmental budget holders operate informal 'back of envelope' systems of recording or estimating forward commitments in order to reduce their own uncertainty regarding possible overspending.

**Consumables.** 'Consumables' are resources whose consumption varies with the number of patients treated, and according to the decisions of doctors, nurses and other NHS professional staff regarding the use of tests, drugs, etc. Variable costs (q.v.) in budgeting and costing may contain some elements of resource use additional to consumables, but these are often difficult to measure. Thus it appears often in pilot systems of clinical budgeting (q.v.) that only consumables are being listed as budget costs over which clinicians are assumed to have direct 'control' as distinct from 'influence'. See 'Griffiths Inquiry Report' and 'Management budgeting'.

**Contracting out.** 'Contracting out' is different from privatization (q.v.). It involves taking some service or function necessary to the NHS and offering it on precise contract terms (of standards of quality and of efficiency) to the lowest bidder who meets the standards. Bidders can be representatives of existing staff, or private firms, preferably with specialist expertise.

The NHS has always 'contracted out' or 'bought in' various of its essential services and supplies. Economy of cost to agreed standards is an important criterion, and it seems relevant where standards can be precisely monitored and workers are not in direct contact with patients, for example laundry, catering or even pathology. But where services do involve direct contact with patients (e.g. medical and nursing care, and also the work of cleaners and others who attend in wards and theatres) there is an additional dimension of human confidence and shared roles which needs to be taken into consideration, in addition to comparative costs.

**Control.** 'Control' is defined as making sure that performance conforms to plan. This relates both to the control of costs and cash expenditure, and to the control of workload and output to meet targets. It is possible to measure or monitor performance without an agreed plan, but this is largely meaningless in terms of managerial motivation and accountability.

The Griffiths Inquiry Report (q.v.) distinguished between costs which could be 'controlled' by clinicians (i.e. largely consumables (q.v.) but in future possibly also involving levels and costs of nursing care etc.) and costs which could be 'influenced' by clinicians. If one takes a planning and budgeting time horizon of at least a year, then clinical 'influence' could extend even to the indirect fixed costs, including levels of staffing and equipment in wards, theatres and supporting diagnostic and paramedical services.

**Cost and costing.** 'Cost' is the measure of value of resources lost as they are used or consumed in the activities of an organization. 'Cost' is to be distinguished from 'expenditure', which is the exchange of cash or credit to obtain resources. Thus the purchase of a supply of chemicals is an 'expenditure'. This turns into a 'cost' only gradually over a period of time, as the chemicals are consumed in daily batches in laboratories.

'Costing' is the process of measuring and recording costs, usually on an ongoing basis called a 'costing system', hence functional costing (q.v.), patient costing (q.v.), specialty costing (q.v.), etc. See also 'Direct costs', 'Fixed costs', 'Full cost', 'Indirect costs', 'Marginal cost', 'Opportunity costs', 'Standard costs', and 'Variable cost'.

**Cost-benefit analysis.** 'Cost-benefit analysis' (CBA) is an economist's technique for assessing the overall or 'net' merit of a particular activity, organization or service. It can be applied to existing activities, but its principal application is for assessing alternative new developments as part of the planning process. The analysis usually includes wider social costs additional to the obvious 'out-of-pocket' monetary costs. Because the analysis is applied typically for activities which do not produce the benefit of monetary sales income, it follows that the benefits have to be quantified as monetary values imputed to health care and wider social benefits. CBA studies can be useful to decision-makers, although their findings are generally rather subjective and cannot be proven accurate. The philosophy and approach of CBA is used also in option appraisal (q.v.) and QALYs (q.v.).

Drummond M. and Mooney G. (1981). Economic appraisal in health care. *Hospital and Health Services Review* (in 2 parts, October and December).

**Cost centre.** A 'cost centre' is any identifiable grouping of activity, or organizational unit, for which it may be deemed useful to classify cost and workload information. Often a cost centre may be coterminous with a 'budget centre', i.e. the area of cost responsibility of a single budget holder, but sometimes there is improvement of management control information if budgets are subdivided into several cost centres. For example, one nursing officer may hold the budget covering several wards, but it will probably prove useful in future for each ward to be a separate cost centre, or even for each group of patients classified by specialty or DRG to be treated as a separate cost centre. This is not just for fine-tuning of monitoring and control of nursing costs, in this particular example, but also to assist more accurate cost recharging to clinicians or other holders of user budgets (q.v.). Rather similarly, it may be helpful for the head of a service such as pathology to have the overall budget subdivided into separate cost centres based on particular machines, particular teams of staff, or particular types of tests or services.

**Cost improvement programmes.** The Griffiths Inquiry Report (q.v.) recommended that formal 'cost improvement programmes' should be developed throughout the NHS, and this was authorized in HC(84)2. The idea is that each tier in the NHS should consciously budget each year for cost savings of, say, $\frac{1}{2}$% to 1% of revenue budget. The exact sources of intended savings have to be agreed and specified in advance, and the achievement of savings has to be monitored and may be subject to performance review. The savings are intended to be spent on approved new developments and priority areas generally. The savings are intended to be made through increased efficiency, without cuts in the volume or essential standards of care.

  Achieving this latter condition becomes increasingly difficult after a few years, and auditors have concluded the condition has already been breached in a number of districts. This Griffiths initiative has probably benefited NHS productivity in the short term with little loss in quality of patient care, but for the longer term it will either have to be abandoned or have the percentage target for annual cost savings cut substantially. See 'Performance' and 'VFM'.

**Cost (and budget) variances.** 'Cost variances' are the numerical differences between actual costs (q.v.) and standard costs (q.v.). Cost variances can be expressed as an amount of money per unit of resources used, or per unit of output achieved (e.g. an X-ray, a test, or a case treated). 'Budget variances' are the total difference over a period of time, typically a month, between the funds budgeted and the costs charged (i.e. either actual costs or standard costs) for the volume of workload achieved.

**Cross-charging.** See 'Recharging'.

**Depreciation.** 'Depreciation' is the estimated cost for the wearing-out of fixed/capital assets such as equipment, plant and vehicles. There are several methods of calculating depreciation, but to take a simple example of the straight-line method, suppose an item of laboratory equipment is bought for £10,000, has an expected useful life of five years and is not expected to have any salvage or trade-in value at the end of that life. It follows that the annual depreciation will be £2,000 (i.e. £10,000 divided by 5 years), and of course this can be divided by twelve to provide the monthly depreciation charge properly chargeable to the responsible budget holder. As stated, depreciation is an estimated figure, as there are always uncertainties regarding the useful life of a machine or vehicle, its future salvage or trade-in value, and the effects of technological change and inflation upon its life and future replacement cost.

At present the NHS does not calculate depreciation costs and charge these to budget holders, but trials are in progress and this system, common in industry, may become universal in the NHS sometime in the 1990s. The quantity and costliness of capital assets is thought to vary widely among different hospitals and districts. Therefore without the inclusion of depreciation cost the comparison of unit costs (q.v.), specialty costs (q.v.) and other measures of cost and budgetary performance between different hospitals and districts may not be clearly meaningful.

Lapsley I. (1981). A case for depreciation accounting in UK health authorities. *Accounting and Business Research*.

**Diagnosis related groups.** 'Diagnosis related groups' (commonly known as DRGs) is the name of a system of classifying acute, non-psychiatric inpatients according to their diagnostic characteristics and related health care resource requirements. DRGs were developed in the USA after years of research. Under the system a standard cost has been determined for each of the 457 DRGs which is used in the USA as the prospective reimbursement price by which American acute hospitals are paid for treatment provided to Medicare patients (i.e. the elderly). The DRG system is now under test in Europe and elsewhere, and in the UK there are several research projects, some of which have concern for the comparative cost of treating different DRGs.

The use of DRGs can be linked with patient costing (q.v.) and case mix costing and budgeting (q.v.). Software is available from the DHSS which enables any health authority to access HAA data stored on regional computers, in order to obtain analyses of case mix classified by DRGs for non-psychiatric acute inpatients. Costs to match against the DRGs will not be routinely available at least before the mid 1990s, but estimates can be made now, and some of the new resource management (q.v.) projects are expected to attempt the matching of costs and DRGs to find out if this is information which doctors and nurses, and other managers, find useful. See 'CASPE'. *only Sunkerbslots acente cos*

Bardsley M., Coles J. and Jenkins L. (1987). *DRGs and Health Care: The Management of Case Mix*. King Edward's Hospital Fund for London.

*Diagnosis Related Groups Newsletter* edited by Jenkins L. (produced three times a year and circulated free of charge). CASPE Research, London.

Sanderson H.F. and Andrews V. (date unknown). *Monitoring Hospital Services* (an application of DRGs to hospital discharge data in England and Wales). Department of Community Medicine, London School of Hygiene and Tropical Medicine.

**Direct costs.** 'Direct costs' are those costs of resources used which can be directly traced to the decisions and/or personal accountability of identified budget holders. This will normally include the pay of staff directly controlled, consumables used by oneself and one's staff, and the volume costs of tests, X-rays and other services which the budget holder and his/her staff request and obtain. See 'Indirect costs'.

**DRGs.** See Diagnosis related groups.

**Economy.** 'Economy' is cutting expenditure, cost or waste. The concept says nothing about volume or quality of service or workload. See also 'Effectiveness' and 'Efficiency'. Together these comprise the 'Three Es'.

**Effectiveness.** Measuring 'effectiveness' involves assessing performance related to policy objectives, operational targets or quality standards. It is concerned with outcomes (q.v.) rather than with routine outputs (q.v.) like bed days used or numbers of tests done. It involves concepts similar to 'cost-benefit analysis' (q.v.). 'Cost effectiveness' studies compare effectiveness or benefit achieved with the cost of resources used in that achievement. See also 'Economy' and 'Efficiency'.

**Efficiency.** Unlike economy (q.v.), 'efficiency' does not necessarily involve or imply the cutting of expenditure or cost. Efficiency is concerned with improving the performance relationship between inputs of resources consumed and outputs of workload accomplished. In the NHS, with its unmet demand and need for health care services, the emphasis will normally be on increasing the outputs (i.e. treatments, operations, bed days provided, etc.) rather than cutting inputs. But this does involve using the input resources more economically (e.g. minimizing the time when beds or theatres are empty, since high fixed costs or standby costs are incurred, with no benefit, when any NHS facility is not being actively used). See also 'Effectiveness', which is concerned with the quality or benefit of outcomes of health care. Effectiveness is highly relevant for planning and performance review, but efficiency is the more relevant concept for day-to-day operational management, and for cost and budgetary control.

**Estate.** The NHS 'estate' comprises its stock of land and buildings. No accurate valuation exists for the NHS estate, but it seems quite likely that the market value of its land, plus the replacement cost of its hospitals and other buildings, may exceed £30 billion. For some years the NHS has been cutting the number of hospital beds, mainly by closing older or less efficient hospitals, especially the large, Victorian long-stay hospitals. The government has been keen to see surplus land and buildings sold off, both to reduce property management and maintenance costs, and to release capital funds which could be redeployed to new hospitals within the NHS.

The Ceri Davies Report (q.v.) arose partly from this concern. The Körner (q.v.) programme was also concerned with the problem of lack of cost information on the estate and commissioned an AHST (q.v.) working party to report on this. A more general concern is that, owing to the tightness of funding of the NHS, funds needed for the maintenance of NHS buildings, plant and equipment are having to be diverted to maintain the volume and standards of patient care.

AHST Capital and Asset Accounting Working Party (1985). *Managing Capital Assets in the National Health Service* CIPFA, London.
DHSS (1983). *Underused & Surplus Property in the National Health Service*, Report of the inquiry chaired by Ceri Davies, DHSS, London.

**Expenditure.** 'Expenditure' means money spent. Normally this means 'cash spending from resource allocations expressed as cash limits'. See 'Cash accounting/budgets/limits', but see also 'Income and expenditure accounting' in which simple cash accounting is amended by the principles of Accural accounting (q.v.).

**Facilities.** The term 'facilities' has now been adopted to identify physical premises and organizational work groups which provide direct, hands-on care of patients (i.e. mainly wards, operating theatres and clinics). This is an important classification for management budgeting (q.v.) because the method of calculating costs, and the identification of accountability for workload and costs, may differ considerably between the facilities and other service departments (q.v.) such as pathology where services are for patient care purposes, but are at one degree removed from patient contact.

**Feeder systems.** 'Feeder systems' are the supporting information systems needed to 'feed in' accurate data on staff utilization, workload, patient administration, use of facilities (q.v.) and service departments (q.v.), etc. in order to have all the information available to compile accurate specialty costs, clinical management costs and budgets, or patient costs and case mix budgets. All major feeder systems need to be on computer, for economy in the handling of the volume of data, and for promptness and flexibility in providing outputs of useful data for costing and budgeting control. In the Griffiths (q.v.) trials of management budgeting, there seemed to be wide agreement that up to 80% of the start-up costs of providing clinical budgets was money spent on computerizing and improving the speed and accuracy of data in the necessary feeder systems.

**Financial accountability.** See 'Accountability' for definition. It is axiomatic that every employee of every type of organization must 'account for' the quantity and quality of work done, even if in practice this usually means other clerical or specialist staff monitoring and reporting on his or her work, with answerability or accountability for this to some higher level in the organization. Of course the situation becomes confused for senior professional staff in hospitals and universities, where there may be claims that accountability for the *quality* of work done can only be assessed by professional peers. But as regards the *volume* of work done and the resources (and their financial cost) consumed in doing that work, there really can be no dispute that all staff, even of the highest professional grades, must be financially accountable. Otherwise, *force majeure*, the parent organization will probably cut the financial resources made available.

**Financial Information Project.** The Financial Information Project (FIP) is based at the West Midlands RHA. It is a research programme which has been operational for about eight years, funded by the DHSS as well as NHS sources. Its main themes have been patient costing (q.v.) or 'patient-based information systems'. It has developed these both for acute services and for the community services.

In a similar spirit to Körner (q.v.) the FIP has sought to bring together information on activity, manpower and finance in a single or integrated information system. The FIP has recognized that it is not feasible to develop or instal a total healthcare management information system 'all at one go', and it has specialized in certain 'modules' of such a system. Its most publicized work has been in information systems for ward nursing, for operating theatres, and for community services. These all involve the use of computers for data and for report preparation.

Two introductory reports on the work of the FIP are listed below, but the full list of its publications and the available computer systems and user manuals, etc., is too lengthy to include here. Interested readers should write to the Financial Information Project, Alpha Tower, Suffolk Street Queensway, Birmingham B1 2JP.

Greenhalgh C.A. (1985). Patient based information systems – something for everyone. *Hospital and Health Services Review.*
Greenhalgh C.A. (1986). Management information initiatives in the NHS. *Public Finance & Accountancy.*

**Financial Management Initiative.** The 'Financial Management Initiative' (FMI) is the name of a new system introduced to the Civil Service and supporting services from about 1980. It includes the development of better management information systems, more detailed costing, budgetary accountability devolved to lower levels of line management, and increased use of performance indicators and reviews. In short, the FMI is in most respects directly comparable to the developments in the NHS described in this book.

**FIP.** See 'Financial Information Project'.

**Fixed budgets.** 'Fixed budgets' are budgets which specify a maximum amount of cash expenditure over the specified time period of the budget. This is the normal type of budget used throughout the public sector, at least where cash limits (q.v.) are imposed by central government. Certainly the annual resource allocation (q.v.) to each health authority is in effect a fixed budget at the organizational level of the district as a whole. But it is possible for budgets *within* districts (and regions for regional services) to be more flexible in order to react to changes in the *relative* workloads of individual departments, specialties, etc. See 'Flexed/flexible budgets'.

**Fixed costs.** 'Fixed costs' are costs which continue at a constant level or rate over an extended period of time (e.g. a budget year). In the NHS the major 'fixed costs' comprise staff pay, which is nearly 75% of total cost. And indeed in many NHS departments with career staff, pay will prove to be a fixed or constant cost over the full year. But of course, at the level of the authority as a whole, there are bound to be many staff departures during the year, especially from ancillary and nursing payrolls, so that even pay costs need not be considered as totally 'fixed'. When staff depart, districts can hold non-essential posts vacant for an extended period, if necessary, to avoid overspending. See 'Variable costs'.

**Flexed/flexible budgets.** 'Flexible budgets', also called 'flexed budgets', are the opposite of fixed budgets (q.v.). Under flexible budgeting all those costs which vary with the volume of treatment provided – mainly consumables in the NHS – are separated from the fixed costs for purposes of budget setting and monitoring. The fixed costs continue to be budgeted as a fixed, total amount of cost allowable over the budget year. But the variable costs are budgeted instead on the basis of the allowable cost for each unit of treatment, or test, or occupied bed day, or otherwise as appropriate to the key workload indicators of each separate budget holder. Then, as workload rises or falls in particular departments, wards, specialties, etc., from month to month through the budget year, the variable component of each budget is 'flexed' automatically so that the flexible budgets rise or fall in direct proportion to the workload dealt with.

Of course, if most services increase their workloads beyond the planning basis for the budget year, there would be pressure on the district to overspend its cash limit (q.v.). Presumably the risk of this happening is why most NHS treasurers do not like to use flexible budgets for their budget holders, although unit financial advisors and treasurers should always be approachable to discuss the possibility of additional budget funds in genuine cases where workload simply *must* be expanded beyond the budget planning basis (of cases treated, bed days occupied, etc.).

**FMI.** See 'Financial Management Initiative'.

**Full cost.** 'Full cost' is the total cost of completing a single unit, or other specified volume, of work done. It is the sum of fixed costs and variable costs. Alternatively it can be viewed as the sum of direct and indirect costs including overheads (although sometimes overheads may be omitted on the grounds that they are not under the control or even the influence of the manager or other budget holder). Full cost (preferably with overheads included) can be used as the basis for setting rates or prices for recharging (q.v.) between units, districts or regions on a long-term basis – although on a shorter-term basis it may often prove more efficient for the NHS as a whole if recharges are made at a lower price, nearer to marginal cost (q.v.).

**Functional costs and budgets.** Costing and budgeting systems should always reflect organizational structure. When the organization of the NHS was changed in 1974 to focus financial responsibility on the heads of 'functions' (i.e. specialized professional services such as nursing), 'functional costs and budgets' were introduced to help monitor compliance with budget limits by heads of functions. Officers heading functions could subdivide budgets for the day-to-day administration of 'delegated budget holders' (e.g. nursing officers at each hospital site), but in most districts power over budgets appeared to remain firmly centralized (e.g. control over virement (q.v.)).

Later, the effect of the 1982 reorganization with the creation of units, and then the effect of the Griffiths recommendation to introduce general managers down to (and importantly including) units, combined to require more genuine decentralization of cost and budget systems down to unit level basis. See 'Unit management costs and budgets'.

Developments in costing and/or budgeting by specialty, by clinician or by DRG/case mix workloads appear more likely to provide management information and control additional to, rather than in place of, existing unit functional costing and budgeting.

**General management.** The 'general management' approach has been introduced to the NHS as the major innovation from the Griffiths Inquiry Report (q.v.). The approach involves two main concepts. The first is that every senior officer/manager should see himself or herself as committed to the efficiency and effectiveness of the total organization and its goals, more than to the interests of individual functions or professions. This is not easy to achieve, for most officers/managers have grown up within the culture of separated, functional professions.

This makes the second concept all the more important: that each major operational entity in the NHS, from the level of units upwards, should be headed by a general manager. The general manager is meant to take a balanced overview of all the functions, professions and activities in the NHS, to give strong leadership towards change and progress, to emphasize the external objectives of improving care and service, and to make good use of all available management techniques to advance efficiency and effectiveness.

**Griffiths Inquiry Report.** The Griffiths Inquiry (officially known as the NHS Management Inquiry) reported on 6 October 1983 in the form of a detailed letter addressed to the Secretary of State. It included supporting argument to principal recommendations covering the establishment of the new Health Services Supervisory Board and the NHS Management Board, the reform of functional management in favour of general management (q.v.), the increased delegation of control and accountability for budgets to units (see 'unit management costs and budgets'), the improvement of personnel services and management and of property (i.e. estate) management, the introduction of annual cost improvement programmes (q.v.), and the introduction of management budgeting (q.v.).

Griffiths R. (1983). *The NHS Management Inquiry Report*. DHSS.
DHSS (1984). Health Services Management – Implementation of the NHS Management Inquiry Report. *DHSS HC(84)13*.

**Healthcare Financial Management Association (HFMA).** See 'Association of Health Service Treasurers'.

**Income and expenditure accounting.** 'Income and expenditure accounting' is the name of the system of accounting used in the NHS for its internal or management accounts, and for its most important external financial reports. See 'Accrual accounting'. Health authorities additionally have to prepare accounts on a cash basis, to prove compliance with cash limits (q.v.).

In the non-statutory simplified annual accounts increasingly provided by treasurers for information to health authority members, employees and the local community, a report known as the sources and applications of funds statement is used frequently as a means of explaining, or reconciling, the differences between the final results in the cash limits accounts for the year, compared to the income and expenditure accounts. Typically the main differences between the two sets of accounts derive from differing treatments of changes in the year-on-year balances in accounts for debtors, creditors and stocks of consumables. See 'Cash accounting/budgets/limits'.

**Incremental budgeting.** Prior to the introduction of the cash limits (q.v.) system of public sector funding from April 1976 – and indeed for years after that until the combination of reduced funding growth and tighter control on the enforcement of cash limits began to bite – 'incremental budgeting' was the typical procedure for budget preparation in the NHS. Under this procedure the size of the existing budget for a particular function was not usually challenged but was instead accepted as the 'baseline' for the next year's budget. To this baseline was then added adjustment for inflation. There could be further addition for a share in 'growth money'. It is argued that this method of budgeting encourages complacency, inefficiency and rigidity.

At the opposite extreme is zero-base budgeting (q.v.). This approach may be too extreme, but the essence of the argument is that all budgets should be open to challenge, debate and reconsideration from year to year, in the light of available resources and evolving awareness of both changing priorities and opportunities for the more efficient use of resources. See 'Cash accounting/budgets/limits'.

**Indirect costs.** 'Indirect costs' are those costs of resources used which cannot be traced or identified in any direct manner to the decisions and/or personal accountability of particular budget holders. Examples include the fixed costs of service departments, wards and theatres, where an establishment, or pool, of human and equipment resources is provided in readiness to serve the needs of patients in various clinical specialties. See 'Direct costs'.

Whereas direct costs can be directly allocated, indirect costs have to be recharged on some basis of estimation or approximation, called apportionment (q.v.). Most indirect costs (e.g. the volume and cost of nurse staffing) can be influenced by the decisions and behaviour of the holders of user budgets, such as clinicians taking part in management budgeting (q.v.). But some indirect costs, the overheads (q.v.) like heating, building maintenance and grass mowing, are so remote from the influence of operational budget holders as to be hardly worth apportionment, so the cost will be arbitrarily recharged.

**Information technology.** The main current and potential financial information systems described in this book (e.g. specialty costing, patient or case mix costing and budgeting) could not be introduced into the NHS without major growth in the use of computers. Manual processing of data into information and reports would be unacceptably expensive in labour costs, and also the output of reports would be too late for effective management control.

The author is not an expert in 'information technology' (IT), but it seems that there are four main aspects of the use of IT for health services management information. The first three refer to routine information systems: data collection and storage, data processing into a range of regular or special reports, and the infrastructure of terminals and interlinkages which allow different computer systems to collect, share and disgorge data and information.

The fourth main use of computers is in analysis, *ad hoc* problem-solving for planners and decision-makers. In the author's opinion, it is in this latter category that one may include work such as that done by Inter-Authority Comparisons & Consultancy at the HSMC, Birmingham, based on the pioneering work of John Yates; and the work of Exeter Health Information Services Ltd., based on the equally pioneering work of Professor John Ashford. But of course there are innumerable suppliers of IT systems, software and hardware which may be useful to the NHS, and to keep up to date one needs to read regularly the *British Journal of Healthcare Computing*, or consult a reference service such as that listed below.

*Information Technology in Health Care* (1986 plus looseleaf updates). Kluwer Publishing in association with the Institute of Health Services Management.

**Inputs.** 'Inputs' are the human and physical resources committed to, or consumed in, productive work. For financial and managerial control these inputs have to be represented by their monetary costs (e.g. from payroll and the purchase prices of consumables), given that this monetary equivalent is the only 'common denominator' by which resources as different as nursing hours and X-ray tests can be aggregated into a single measure of total resource consumption.

**Interactive Resource Information System.** See 'IRIS'.

**Internal audit.** 'Internal audit' is the ongoing year-round audit checking provided by the audit staff of the health authority. Traditionally internal audit was only concerned with the probity of expenditure, but in recent years the brief has been extended to the assessment of the economy and efficiency of managers' use of resources. See 'Salmon Report' and 'VFM'. See also 'Audit' for the role of external audit as distinguished from internal audit.

NHSTA (1986). *The NHS Internal Audit Manual* (two volumes), with inputs from a NHS project team, the HFMA and Price Waterhouse as consultants to the project. Bristol.

**IRIS.** 'IRIS' is the new 'Interactive Resource Information System' being tested as a successor to the standard accounting system (q.v.). It is intended to be linked with district feeder systems so as to enable a much wider range of management reporting than under the old SAS approach.

IRIS has been dogged by delays, probably owing to its complexity (which is the price paid for a new system intended to be interactive with manpower, management budgeting, payroll and various other information systems). Alternative, possibly less ambitious accounting computer systems have been developed by some regions and by commercial suppliers.

Anslow R. and Jones S. (1986). IRIS blossoms. *British Journal of Healthcare Computing.*

Jones S. and Anslow R. (1985). IRIS: a financial information system for the next decade. *Public Finance & Accountancy.*

**Körner.** Mrs Edith Körner chaired the NHS/DHSS Steering Group on Health Services Information and the reports of this Group are usually referred to as Körner Reports. The Steering Group sought simplification, standardization of minimum data requirements (and thus more comparable information outputs), and improved management information for NHS management (especially control and performance information for use by operational levels of management in all disciplines). The Steering Group worked under the constraints that its recommendations should not greatly increase the clerical or management costs of the NHS, and that its brief did not include the linked issues of co-ordinating management data collecting and reporting with the strategic development of the use of computers and computer systems.

The Körner programme produced six main reports (but see also 'Asset accounting'). Four of these reports largely concentrated on activity and workload measures for clinical and other services. One report specialized on manpower information. The Sixth Report covered financial information. Most of the Sixth Report related to technical points mainly of interest only to finance staff, but included was the major recommendation to introduce specialty costing (q.v.) as a routine measurement and reporting system in the NHS. The analysis and understanding of management performance and resource use (and needs) requires the constant interlinkage of the three types of data and information: activity/workload, manpower and finance.

DHSS (1984). *Health Services Development*, Reports of the Steering Group on Health Services Information: Implementation Programme, HC(84)10; and *Health Services Management*, Reports of the Steering Group on Health Services Information: Implementation Programme, HC(84)13.

NHS/DHSS Steering Group on Health Services Information (1984). *Sixth Report* (On the Collection and Use of Financial Information). HMSO.

Mason A. and Morrison V. (eds.) (1985). *Walk, Don't Run*, essays on NHS information issues. King Edward's Hospital Fund for London.

Windsor P. (1986). *Introducing Körner*. BJHC Books (British Journal of Healthcare Computing).

**Magee specialty costing.** Professor Charles Magee was the pioneer of low cost specialty costing information based largely on sampling and estimation, not accurate enough for use in specialty budgeting, but useful for planning and for *ad hoc* inquiries into the efficiency and effectiveness of resource use. The research of Magee at Bridgend Hospital was financed by the DHSS, which subsequently financed trials in eight hospitals. The results of this were promising, and were commended to the Körner programme. It is a matter of personal regret to this author that the Körner Sixth Report on Financial Information in the NHS recommended the adoption of Magee's form of specialty costing, but without acknowledging Professor Magee's name or contribution to the evolution of NHS information. See 'Specialty costing and budgeting'.

Magee C.C. (1981). The potential for specialty costing in the NHS. *Public Finance and Accountancy*.

**Management accounting.** 'Management accounting' is the use of information on workload and costs, and the analysis of that information, to assist managers at all levels to make best use of the available resources. This emphasizes advising and helping budget holders, but of course it also involves monitoring the performance of budget holders and other managers so that current resource-use problems can be sorted out quickly, and also so that more accurate and realistic decisions can be taken on future budget needs. This role is increasingly taken by unit financial advisers. But there is a continuing problem in that many districts do not have sufficient funds to employ many management accountants, with the result that the time available for financial advice within units is far less than needed to facilitate the progress of new developments in specialty costing (q.v.), management budgeting (q.v.), etc.

Drury C. (1985). *Management and Cost Accounting*. Van Nostrand Reinhold (UK), Wokingham.
Emmanuel C. and Otley D. (1985). *Accounting for Management Control*. Van Nostrand Reinhold (UK), Wokingham.

**Management budgeting.** A major recommendation of the Griffiths Inquiry Report (q.v.) was the introduction of 'management budgeting' throughout the NHS. The general concept here was that budgets should be more than statements of financial allocations and outturn: they should become active management tools, closely monitored and with results reviewed for performance assessment. But in addition it was recommended that clinicians, as decision-makers controlling or influencing the rate of use of NHS resources, should become budget holders, with their own clinical budgets or clinical management budgets (CMB).

Four districts began development of CMBs late in 1983, and possibly twenty or more additional districts have started work on CMBs more recently. Progress in development has been slow, however, partly owing to the large volume of work needed to improve and computerize supporting feeder systems (q.v.), and partly owing to a lack of sufficient senior finance staff in the demonstration districts to interest, educate and involve clinical staff in the new budgeting system and its potential for providing useful information.

The falling cost of computing and the gradual improvement of feeder systems (partly to meet the Körner requirements) will make the universal use of CMBs feasible within a few years, if clinicians agree to participate. Meanwhile, emphasis has shifted to the new initiative in resource management (q.v.).

Brooks R. (ed.) (1986). *Management Budgeting in the NHS*. Health Services Manpower Review, University of Keele.

DHSS (1985). *Management Budgeting in the NHS: Interim Report on Progress and Proposals for Further Development*. DHSS HN(85)3.

DHSS (1986). *Resource Management (Management Budgeting) in Health Authorities*. DHSS HN(86)34.

North Western RHA (1985). *Management Budgeting: an Information Pack for Clinicians* (and various related supporting documentation prepared by the District Support Team). Manchester.

**Management by objectives.** Budgeting (q.v.) casts a broad light over all the workload and resource use of a manager, with emphasis perhaps almost inevitably focusing on the bottom line, the comparison of total cost or expenditure against total budget allocation. In contrast, 'management by objectives (MBO) is a system for focusing a narrow spotlight on just a few managerial objectives or activities at any one time. MBO is a complement to budgeting, not a substitute.

A manager is asked to take one or two important activities or criteria of performance relevant to objectives, and over a period of six months or up to twelve months work to see how much improvement can be achieved. The criteria must be measurable for objective assessment; for example, improving staff morale is difficult to measure, but change in staff turnover rate is easy to measure.

MBO implicitly involves a personal contract between a manager and his or her boss to achieve certain improvements within a limited period of time, and the system will work only if bosses take an interest, monitor results, and provide a de-briefing of constructive assessment at the end of each episode of MBO activity.

Humble J. (1970). *Management by Objectives in Action*. McGraw Hill, London.

**Management Information Pilot Project.** The 'Management Information Pilot Project' (MIPP) was started in 1983 in Bromsgrove and Redditch Health District as a trial to assess the feasibility and value of the information systems recommended in the Körner (q.v.) reports. The objective of MIPP was to develop systems to enable Körner recommendations to be implemented even in districts lacking substantial computing infrastructure. And these new systems should be capable of adoption by other districts quickly and inexpensively.

The development of MIPP was assisted by Price Waterhouse Management Consultants, and it is said that this project was the first to achieve full operational compliance with the Körner requirements. This involves providing necessary information in five main areas: hospital inpatient activity, finance, manpower, hospital facilities and services, and community health services. A series of brochures and papers is available from the DHSS to document the work and implementation of the MIPP, including a layman's guide to the MIPP systems. MIPP shares with FIP (q.v.) the distinction of being pioneers in the development of better management information systems for community care.

Clarke D. (1986). Community Körner data. *British Journal of Healthcare Computing.*
DHSS (1984). *Management Information Pilot Project – Bromsgrove and Redditich Health Authority.* HC(84)10 – Annex.
DHSS (1985). *A Layman's Guide to the MIPP Systems.* The DHSS Health Services Information Branch.

**Marginal cost.** 'Marginal cost' is a term from economics, where it defines the net increase or decrease in total cost caused by increasing or reducing output (q.v.) by one unit. The term is used also in accounting, where it means the average variable cost (q.v.) of an average unit of output. The figures provided by the economist and the accountant will usually differ. In everyday use 'marginal cost' is often mentioned more loosely, typically to denote the extra cost (or the savings) from some specified change in existing resource use or output. Given this variety in the use of the term, experts providing information under this label should always be challenged to clarify what they mean, and to confirm that their figures contain all the costs, and only those costs, which are actually expected to change if a particular decision is taken.

**MBO.** See 'Management by objectives'.

**Medical audit.** 'Medical audit' traditionally defines the process of peer group review of the diagnosis and treatment patterns employed by a clinician. This has been mainly concerned with the quality of work done and the likely outcome in health terms. There is the possibility in future that medical audits will also include review of the efficiency and effectiveness of resource use in treating particular types of patients. Developments such as DRGs (q.v.) and patient costing (q.v.) will assist this.

**NHS/DHSS Steering Group on Health Services Information.** See 'Körner'.

**Nursing dependency.** 'Nursing dependency' studies aim to establish the different amounts of nursing care or nursing resources required by different categories of patients. Patients can be classified into categories by reference to routine data from nursing records, by judgements made by nurses, or by reference to case mix classifications anyway increasingly being made as part of a wider assessment of treatment needs, resource needs and costs (see 'DRGs' and 'Case mix costing and budgeting'). The latter option probably offers the more objective, long-term method, but in the meantime nursing dependency assessment systems such as pioneered in Cheltenham and developed by the FIP (q.v.) at Coventry and elsewhere should be encouraged.

Nursing dependency information will assist not only in clinical budgeting or case mix costing and budgeting, but also in helping plan, monitor and control the staffing of hospitals in terms of the numbers, skills and grades of nurses needed overall and on individual wards to balance the goals of meeting patient needs relative to economy in nursing costs.

**Opportunity costs.** Typically, resources are limited but the alternative uses for them are numerous. If decisions commit resources to one activity, other uses will have to be forgone. The alternative with the highest net benefit (i.e. excess of 'value' of outcomes over costs or resource commitments) which has to be forgone, defines the 'opportunity cost' (or, the 'sacrifice' cost) of the decision we take.

In practical terms, this concept from economics warns us always to seek out and evaluate all alternatives, or options, before commitment to final decisions. It is especially relevant to the planning of new developments and capital programmes (see 'Option appraisal'), because the time-span and costliness of decisions in these areas are likely to be particularly burdensome and difficult to reverse if delayed awareness of the opportunity costs arises.

**Option appraisal.** 'Option appraisal' is similar in concept to cost-benefit analysis (q.v.). Option appraisal is intended to be a thorough and rigorous assessment of the likely benefits relative to costs of new developments, especially those initiatives involving substantial capital (q.v.) outlays. It is implicit that decision-makers should seek out all the 'options' available, and then assess their relative merit as objectively as possible. In practice some options may not be perceived or admitted, and decisions may be biased by local managerial or political pressures.

Option appraisal is easy to use only in cases where the outcomes or quality of care/service are unchanged, and the problem is simply that of comparing alternative means of providing the same inputs (q.v.) to health care. Thus it is fairly easy to conduct an option appraisal on the degree of desirability of investing a specified sum of capital in new boilers to utilize a cheaper fuel (note this involves the use of discounted cash flow analysis at the rate of interest specified in the TDR (q.v.)).

In contrast, it is not easy to prepare an objective and conclusive option appraisal on the cost-effectiveness plus quality-effectiveness of the option of caring for the mentally handicapped in the community as compared to continuing care in long-stay hospitals. This is because both the cost factors and the quality-of-life factors are very speculative or problematic until they have been fully tested in practice.

Drummond M.J. (1980). *Principles of Economic Appraisal in Health Care.* Oxford University Press, London.

**Outcomes/outputs.** The final 'outputs' of hospitals are patients discharged (and deaths). There are also 'intermediate outputs' in the form of numbers of operations completed, diagnostic tests done, meals served, etc. These output measures, compared between hospitals or studied in any one hospital by trend analysis over a period of years, can give useful information on comparative efficiency (q.v.), but they tell us little about effectiveness (q.v.). Effectiveness relates to 'outcomes' – that is the results in terms of continuing physical and mental health of the client population following the work of preventive, primary, acute and other health services. The overall objective of the NHS must be to maximize the value of health care 'outcomes' (i.e. some measure combining the quantity and the quality of health services), but of course in practice this is difficult to measure and judgements remain largely subjective. See 'QALYs'.

**Overheads.** 'Overheads' are indirect costs (q.v.) which in no way can be linked objectively with the workload or operational decisions of individual managers or clinical budget holders. Taxes and payments in lieu of rates provide the extreme example. Grass mowing, building repairs, other estate costs, and the expense of meeting statutory financial and activity reporting to regions and the DHSS provide other examples. The Griffiths Inquiry Report (q.v.) recommended that all holders of management budgets should be charged with their share of overheads. This goes against the conventional wisdom which is that it is counterproductive to charge operational budget holders with categories of cost over which they have no control or accountability.

**Patient costing.** 'Patient costing' may be defined as a system for the collection and reporting of the costs of treating identified, individual patients. So far, there is no operational system for doing this routinely in the UK, although it can be done on an estimated basis in research projects. This information could be useful to clinicians for use in medical audits and more general reviews of alternative approaches to regimes of patient management.

For most resource planning and management purposes, the identification of individual patients (by name and case) is presumably irrelevant. What is relevant is the category or type of condition and treatment needs into which an individual patient should be classified, so that resource planning and cost monitoring for the overall case mix in each specialty and hospital can be improved. See 'DRGs', 'FIP' and 'Case mix costing and budgeting'.

**Performance indicators/comparisons/reviews.** Most measures of efficiency (i.e. input/output relationships) can be adopted as 'performance indicators', together with other important measures of the use of resources, such as LOS (length of stay). The government has selected a range of performance indicators tailored to most if not all civil service and other centrally funded and monitored public services. NHS hospital and district performance indicators are provided for study on computer.

Critics may say that these indicators do not take sufficient account of 'outcomes', or quality of care, but the government appears to take them seriously. It is anyway a reasonable assumption that improvements in efficiency (which broadly we can measure) will mostly lead also to improvements in effectiveness or the quality of outcomes. Standardized performance indicators, routinely reported, clearly facilitates 'performance comparisons' between hospitals and between districts. These comparisons may sometimes be imperfect and even unfair at present, but the implementation of the Körner reforms (q.v.) should improve the legitimacy of comparisons, while further progress towards information systems based on DRGs (q.v.) or other forms of case mix costing and budgeting (q.v.) should lead to major improvement in the objectivity and relevance of performance comparisons.

Also it seems probable that all future governments will insist that 'performance reviews' are held, at least annually, for all levels of NHS management from units upwards. Districts or units can of course initiate their own programmes of analysis of performance indicators. Help can be obtained from various consultants, including Inter-Authority Comparisons & Consultancy at the Health Services Management Centre, Birmingham, where systems are based on the pioneering work of John Yates.

**Privatization.** 'Privatization' is different from contracting out (q.v.). Privatization is the sale of publicly owned organizations to private organizations, usually as going concerns complete with premises, equipment, staff in post, and existing sales or service contracts (e.g. as in the cases of British Telecom and British Gas). To date the amount of privatization of NHS activities, as distinct from the contracting out of support services, has been almost nil. For the longer-term future, however, privatization must be seen as a serious possibility, even for complete hospitals. Potential bidders to take over parts of the NHS might include for-profit health management corporations, national charities, local not-for-profit trusts, or even local authorities.

**Programme budgeting.** 'Programme budgeting' involves the allocation or budgeting of resources on the basis of major 'programmes', and in the context of the NHS this involves budgeting by 'health care groups', or priorities. In practice this is difficult. For example, care of the elderly crosses the boundaries between hospital and community (and primary) services. Even within hospitals the elderly are treated in most specialties, not just in geriatrics. Given that there are not usually any operational managers of 'programmes', but instead managers of units and of service departments, it is not surprising that programme budgeting has not proved practicable in operational management, even if it may be useful in strategic planning.

**QALYs and quality assurance.** 'QALYs' means 'quality-adjusted life years'. It is intended to be a measure not just of the probable life expectancy (or survival) results from particular medical or surgical interventions, but also a measure which incorporates a weighting factor for the 'quality of life' during the survival period.

QALYs are a concept from health economics, based on concepts shared with cost-benefit analysis (q.v.) and option appraisal (q.v.). These concepts are intellectually sound, in the context of the 'greatest good for the greatest number', but they may seem 'Orwellian'. That is, the use of QALYs may be both rational and humane at the level of planning the allocation and budgeting of health service resources, but at the level of the individual clinician confronted with the individual patient the concept may seem inhumane and irrelevant. This may arise where the resources available are strictly limited and inadequate to meet need or demand. An example may be renal failure.

QALYs are one important approach to measuring health care outcomes (q.v.). QALYs should not be confused with 'quality assurance' (see 'CASPE'). Quality assurance involves the monitoring or testing of performance in the provision of health care, not just in terms of outcomes, but mainly as measured by the quality of the outputs (q.v.) provided by doctors, wards, theatres and service departments.

Gudex C. (1986). *QALYs and Their Use by the Health Service*, Discussion Paper 20. Centre for Health Economics, University of York.

**RAWP.** See 'Resource Allocation Working Party'.

**Real terms.** 'Real terms' is an expression from economics. It recognizes that money, or cash, has no value in itself. Its value lies only in 'terms' (i.e. measurement) of the 'real' (i.e. actual or physical) resources which can be obtained in exchange for a given amount of money or cash. Thus 'real terms' means 'after adjusting for the effects of inflation on prices and payroll'.

But the NHS is financed by 'cash limits' funding allocations which incorporate government planning targets on levels of pay. Government estimates of the planned growth in the NHS, in 'real terms', are derived from their own assumptions for the cash limits (q.v.) calculation. If pay rises, adjustments to working hours requiring extra staff, or price movements in the industries supplying the NHS with other resources, move upwards faster than anticipated by the government in setting its cash limit, then the NHS may find that its growth of 'real resources' (i.e. people and things) turns out much less, in 'real terms', than was officially forecast.

**Recharging.** 'Recharging' is sometimes termed 'cross-charging' in the NHS, and in the academic literature of economics and accounting it is termed 'transfer pricing'. When costs are incurred in the NHS, they are 'charged' against the relevant budget in the host unit, district or region. 'Recharging' involves the original cost, or 'charge', being passed onwards to some other budget, unit, district or region whose patient(s) have benefited from services provided by the host organization. Thus, basically, a recharge is a price charged from one part of the NHS to another part, for services rendered and received.

In earlier years when resources were more freely available, patient treatments and other services could usually cross district boundaries without challenge, rewarded two years in arrears by adjustments to RAWP (q.v.) cross-boundary flow adjustments. Currently, with resources very tight, there is growing interest and temptation to provide services outside a particular unit or district's area of responsibility only if 'cash' is transferred in reciprocation for services rendered. At the ethical level this may seem sad, but at the economic level of analysis this could be beneficial.

Recharges are in effect a price for a service, and this 'price' can be any figure to which the 'buyer' and 'seller' agree. A price above marginal cost (q.v.) or variable cost (q.v.) can provide an incentive to the providing organization to supply service, assuming that there is spare capacity available. In other words, the use of recharging in the NHS can provide a form of internal market, bringing into use any underused treatment capacity and increasing the volume of treatment to meet the backlog of demand on waiting lists. Hip replacement is an example of a service which could be expanded by using 'recharging' to encourage the more intensive utilization of resources for the sharing of output between districts.

**Reserves.** 'Reserves' are funding allocations or budget allocations held centrally. The use of reserves to keep financial resources available for new clinical developments starting later in the year is legitimate, as also are reserves to meet pay increases and other price increases. But if additional reserves are held at unit or district level, often called contingency reserves, this can be counterproductive. On the one hand, money probably needed for caring services has not been allocated in advance for a planned programme of service. And on the other hand, awareness of money (i.e. funding available within cash limits (q.v.)) held on reserve may lead budget holders to feel that their own overspendings can be 'bailed out' by pleadings for support from the reserves. The reserves can easily prove inadequate.

**Resource allocation.** 'Resource allocation' is the awarding of funding from a higher tier to a lower tier in any bureaucratic organization, such as the NHS. See 'RAWP'. Resource allocation is normally determined either by political decisions or else by some mechanistic formula designed to produce equity. Budgeting (q.v.) is different: it is a negotiated or bargained contract between resource managers at different levels as regards the amount of money to be made available, and the activities to which that money shall be applied. The political choice of framework for resource allocation varies between countries, with important effects on the relative costliness, and sometimes the quality, of health care delivery systems.

Maxwell R.J. (1981). *Health and Wealth*, an International Study of Health Care Spending. Lexington.

**Resource Allocation Working Party.** Concern about regional and other inequalities in health care resources and service provision led to the formation of the 'Resource Allocation Working Party' (RAWP), whose main report appeared in 1976. RAWP produced a formula to 'weight', or adjust, raw population numbers for criteria of health care needs. Applied to the population of each health district, this formula would provide the figure for 'target' funding for each district. The 'actual' funding would grow quickly for districts well below 'target', but slowly for districts at or above 'target' funding entitlements.

The original hope was that the equalization or convergence of actual funding of all districts could be brought in line with their 'targets' by about 1990. But since 1976 the real terms (q.v.) rate of growth in NHS funding has contracted substantially. The RAWP policy of equalization of funding has continued, but in some regions, especially the four Thames Regions, it has recently been possible to move the funding of under-funded districts nearer to their targets only by cutting the real terms funding of other districts. Typically the districts cut have been teaching districts or other inner-city districts where there are social stress and deprivation factors not taken into account in the RAWP formula.

This situation has led to rising concern, and to the government commissioning a Review of RAWP in 1985. The Review was completed in late 1986, and it included recommendations for new research as well as advice that the RAWP formula should not be applied mechanistically at sub-regional level.

DHSS (1976). *Sharing Resources for Health in England*, Report of the Resource Allocation Working Party (the RAWP Report). HMSO.
DHSS (1986). *Review of the Resource Allocation Working Party Formula*, Report by the NHS Management Board. DHSS.
Holland W.W. et al. (1980). *The RAWP Project*. Social Medicine and Health Services Research Unit, St Thomas' Hospital & Medical School.

Royal Commission on the National Health Service (1978). *Allocating Health Resources: a Commentary on the Report of the Resource Allocation Working Party*, Research Paper No. 3. HMSO.

**Resource management.** 'Resource management' is the name given to a new generation of projects to involve doctors and nurses in using financial and other management information to help achieve more efficient and effective use of resources. This new initiative was announced in HN(86)34. Resource management projects may include the development of management budgeting (q.v.), patient costing (q.v.), the use of DRGs (q.v.) in case mix costing and budgeting (q.v.), or other initiatives in the development of better management information of interest to doctors, nurses and/or other health care professions.

DHSS (1986). *Resource Management (Management Budgeting) in Health Authorities*. DHSS, HN(86)34.

**Revenue.** Like most other public services funded by central government, the NHS receives its funding in two separate allocations, 'capital' (q.v.) and 'revenue'. Capital is funding for major new investments in buildings, the initial equipping of buildings and certain other high-cost assets such as mainframe computers. Revenue is funding for the operational running costs of the NHS including the maintenance and the replacement of most types of plant and equipment.

**Royal Commission on the NHS.** The last Royal Commission on the NHS did not say a great deal about financial information and control in its Report. However, it did broadly endorse that the NHS should push ahead with testing the usefulness of the 56 recommendations made in Research Paper No. 2, *Management of Financial Resources in the National Health Service*, which had been prepared at the request of the Royal Commission.

Royal Commission on the National Health Service (1979). *Report*, Cmnd. 7615. HMSO.
Royal Commission on the National Health Service (1978). *The Management of Financial Resources in the National Health Service*, Research Paper No. 2. HMSO.

**Salmon Report.** The 'Salmon Report' was concerned with improving audit (q.v.) in the NHS. It sought improved resources and training for NHS (and DHSS) auditors, the strengthening of skills and staffing in the audit of computer information systems, and the raising of standards in internal audit (q.v.), including the idea that small districts unable to afford substantial internal audit teams should join in consortia with other districts to provide a stronger service with greater specialist expertise in depth (e.g. with computer systems). It also recommended greater attention to the audit of 'value for money' (VFM) (q.v.), and that audit committees should be established by health authorities, at least on a trial basis. These audit committees should be multi-disciplinary in membership and take a particular interest in VFM issues and in providing feedback to the parent authorities regarding possible improvements in management efficiency and effectiveness.

Salmon P. (1983). *Report of the DHSS/NHS Audit Working Group.* DHSS.

**SAS.** See 'Standard accounting system'.

**Service departments.** 'Service departments' is one name for those departments of a hospital which are closely involved with patient treatment but which, unlike facilities (q.v.) such as wards, do not themselves house or tend patients. Diagnostic and paramedical services comprise the main service departments.

In the context of management budgeting, service departments are 'intermediate budget centres'. That is, their costs have to be recharged to the specialties or individual clinicians whose patients receive their services. The heads of service departments remain accountable for their fixed costs (q.v.) of staffing and equipment, but accountability for the variable costs of consumables (i.e. the costs determined by the 'volume' of treatment decided by doctors) will be charged to clinicians. To avoid clinicians wrongly being held accountable for higher costs resulting from purchasing consumables at excessive prices, their clinical budgets (q.v.) should be charged for the use of resources on the basis of standard costs (q.v.).

**SIFT (Service Increment for Teaching).** 'SIFT' is an addition to the annual funding allocations from the DHSS to regions. It is meant to cover the reasonable extra costs incurred by teaching hospitals (i.e. hospitals providing training for undergraduate medical students). The reason for having a special allocation for this is that the number of student places in medical education is not distributed around the country in proportion to the regional populations on which the RAWP formula (q.v.) is based.

There is a widely held view that the SIFT allocation is larger than needed simply to meet the extra expense of training medical students, but also that it is less than needed to fund the extra burden of advanced, experimental and high-tech medicine, and the more complex case mix which teaching hospitals inevitably attract. These problems were examined in detail (with contributions also from the USA and the Netherlands) in a 'Special Issue on Teaching Hospitals' of the journal, *Financial Accountability & Management*, in its Summer 1987 issue (published by Basil Blackwell, Oxford).

**Specialty costing and budgeting.** 'Specialty costing' is the process of allocating or apportioning all hospital costs to each separate specialty according to the actual level of workload it has imposed on wards, theatres, clinics, X-ray, labs and other support services. The method was developed in Wales by Professor C. Magee, piloted in eight English and Welsh hospitals, and adopted by the Körner (q.v.) management information programme as one of its important new requirements. Districts were due to start collecting specialty cost data for hospitals from April 1987, and to start providing annual reports on this from the summer of 1988. Specialty costs will provide information useful for evaluation of performance, and for comparisons between hospitals, although comparisons can only be tentative until information on the case mix or DRGs (q.v.) in each specialty in each hospital is made routinely available.

Specialty budgeting is a form of management budgeting (q.v.) in which the budgets are based on whole specialties rather than individual clinicians.

Like other forms of clinical management budgeting, specialty budgeting requires a much higher standard of accurate recording and prompt processing of activity and workload data (and a higher degree of computerization) than most districts will need simply to comply with the Körner reporting requirements for specialty costs.

The collection of community health services costs on a similar basis will commence from April 1988, using systems such as those developed by MIPP (q.v.).

Carter, J. (1983). *Recent Developments in Financial Information for Management in Health Services*, Warwick Papers in Industry, Business and Administration No. 10. IMRAD, University of Warwick.

Hillman R. (1984). *Specialty Costing in the National Health Service*. AHST/CIPFA.

**Standard accounting system.** The 'standard accounting system' (SAS) is a general ledger accounting system which runs on large main frame computers operated by regional health authorities on behalf of their districts. There is a linked 'standard payroll system'. The main objectives of both systems (which incidentally are not used by all regions) are to ensure that income and expenditure is properly accounted for, and that the information required for statutory reports to government is available and accurate.

Neither of these systems has as a principal objective the provision of information for operational control by local management. However, the successor to SAS, IRIS (q.v.), is being developed with a wider range of outputs potentially useful to managers within units and districts.

**Standard costs.** 'Standard costs' are 'estimated target' costs per unit of workload or output, usually updated at least once a year. When updated, they should take account of inflation and also of known or planned improvements in productivity and efficiency more generally. Accurate standard costs provide a fair basis for recharging the costs of service departments (q.v.) and facilities (q.v.) to specialties (see 'Specialty costing and budgeting') or for management budgeting (q.v.). The amounts recharged to specialties or management budgets under this system are recorded additionally in the accounts of the service departments and facilities as a notional income or valuation of service rendered. The latter can then be compared against the actual operating costs of these departments, the numerical differences being termed variances (q.v.). These variances can be analysed to estimate their causes, as between the effects of inflation and departures from the planned or expected levels of efficiency and volume of service provided (e.g. numbers of diagnostic tests requested by doctors).

**Subjective costs.** The 'subjective' classification of costs involves identifying costs by the 'subject' or type of resource on which expended, e.g. nurses pay, provisions, stationery, etc. This was the main type of costing used in the NHS prior to the 1974 reorganization. The latter introduced functional costing (q.v.). Now Körner has led to specialty costing (q.v.). In time this may evolve further to clinical costing (q.v.) and even patient costing (q.v.) or case mix costing (q.v.) with DRGs (q.v.). Each of these levels of more detailed disaggregation of costs requires additional data, or at least more accurate and precise data promptly processed, and without continuing progress in computerization, these new costing systems would not be feasible or cheaply affordable.

**Sunk costs.** 'Sunk costs' is an economist's term. It refers to past expenditure on resources such as buildings or equipment. Their *original* cost, already paid for, is irrelevant to current and future decisions. What is relevant is the market value for disposing of an existing building or piece of equipment, if surplus, and also the replacement cost of any new building or equipment needed in order to continue planned services.

**TDR (test discount rate).** In the NHS most capital investment is committed to replace, expand or upgrade patient services. A profit or financial return on capital is not sought. The return sought is better health care, but this is difficult to evaluate in terms of monetary benefit.

However, one can attempt to estimate the relative merit of alternative uses of NHS capital funds: see 'Cost-benefit analysis' and 'Option appraisal'. And in some cases it is even possible to assess a financial return on the use of NHS capital. For example, one can assess the return on investment in new boilers capable of using a cheaper source of fuel/energy, the return on purchasing diesel vehicles to replace petrol vehicles, or the return from purchasing any mechanized, labour-saving piece of equipment.

In such cases the NHS, and indeed all other public services, are expected to aim for a financial return at least equal to the 'TDR' before committing capital. The TDR or test discount rate is specified as a 5% return on capital invested. The '5%' is understood to represent roughly what the private sector of the economy is likely to earn (after adjusting for inflation) from a low-risk investment in a competitive market. It is argued that it would be disadvantageous to the economy of the UK if the public sector were allowed to make investments for a lower rate of return, savings or other economic benefit, than experienced in the private sector.

**Transfer pricing.** 'Transfer pricing' is the academic term for cross charging or recharging (q.v.) of costs for services rendered between the budgets of any two parts of the same organization (and here it is reasonable to argue that the NHS overall is but one organization). Academic theory argues that where there is no external market to specify a 'fair price', or to which spare capacity can be 'sold', then it is likely that the economic output of the total organization will be maximized by recharging services at marginal cost (q.v.). Marginal cost in the NHS is typically far below full cost (q.v.), except that once spare capacity is used up then marginal cost itself has to take account of additional fixed costs and capital investment needed to expand workload further.

**Unit costs.** The term 'unit costs' risks confusion. In accounting, 'units' means items of production or of service. Thus 'unit cost' is the cost per item of production or service (i.e. tests, meals, bed-days, operations, etc.). Unit costs can be measured in terms of actual costs (q.v.) or standard costs (q.v.). The confusion can arise because of the NHS organizational tier, 'units' of management. Thus 'unit costs' may sometimes be mentioned to mean the total costs or expenditure of a 'unit' (e.g. a hospital).

**Unit management costs and budgets.** Since the 1982 reorganization and especially since the implementation of the Griffiths Inquiry recommendation that general managers should be appointed, the unit (i.e. typically a major hospital, the community services, or a grouping of small hospitals) has become the key managerial level for operational co-ordination of the use of NHS resources. This necessitates information for both planning and control based on cost data and budgets. Currently the financial information available is in the form of functional costs and budgets (q.v.) but soon Körner specialty costing (q.v.) will become available to assist general managers and other managers in units. Of course, new financial and other management information systems are of little use unless integrated with effective management organization and leadership.

Staff of the Health Services Management Centre, Birmingham (1985: 30 May, 13 June, 27 June, 11 July and 1 August). Unit structure. *Health and Social Services Journal*. (A series of research-based articles).

**User budgets.** 'User budgets' is an alternative name for management budgets (q.v.) held by users of resources. Here 'users' refers to staff who control the volume or rate of resource use in the care of patients. Mainly this means consultants who admit patients, fill beds, order tests and operations, etc.

**Variable cost.** 'Variable cost' is an accounting term which refers to those operational costs which vary more or less directly in proportion to changes in the volume of workload. In practice in the NHS variable costs consist mainly of consumables. Unlike in a factory or a supermarket, the vast majority of NHS costs comprise fixed costs (q.v.), at least between annual planning and budget reviews.

**Variances.** 'Variances' are the numerical differences between planned workload and actual workload, between allowed budgets and actual cost expenditure, between expected standard cost (q.v.) per unit and actual average unit costs, and so forth. The careful analysis of variances helps managers understand and correct developing problems in resource utilization. See 'Cost (and budget) variances'.

**VFM (value for money).** 'Value for money' is a term or concept which is largely self-explanatory. VFM is rated as highly important by the government. In central government VFM is closely associated to the initiative on FMI (q.v.), and to a variety of improvements in budgeting and auditing systems. In the NHS, concern for VFM is manifested through the compulsory annual cost improvement programmes, routine performance reviews and the supply of performance indicators, and the strengthening of the staffing and role of internal audit (q.v.).

Butt, H. and Palmer R. (1985). *Value for Money in the Public Sector*. Basil Blackwell, Oxford.
CIPFA/AHST (1985). *Health Service Value for Money Guide* (two volumes).
National Audit Office (1986). *Value for Money Developments in the National Health Service*, Report by the Comptroller and Auditor General. HMSO.

Price Waterhouse (1983). *Value for Money Auditing Manual.* Gee & Co., London. (With updating supplements.)

**Virement.** 'Virement' is the transfer of spending authority and funds from one budget to another, or from one budget heading or subhead to another. At district level virement can take place between revenue and capital allocations: up to 1% of revenue can be vired to capital, or up to 10% of capital can be vired to revenue, in any one year. At unit level and below, virement is more likely to involve transfers between two separate revenue budgets or headings (e.g. between staff pay and some category of consumables).

**Ward budgeting.** When Griffiths-style management budgeting (q.v.) is adopted, it is essential that accurate costing and budgeting is introduced for all service departments (q.v.) and facilities (q.v.). In most hospitals the most costly facilities are wards. But of course one can have budgets and the reporting of costs for wards even where management budgeting is not in use. Pioneering work on ward budgeting has been done in Manchester. Possibly the most advanced systems for ward budgeting and costing, including the use of ward-based computer terminals, have been developed by the FIP (q.v.).

**Workload budgeting and resource allocation.** 'Workload budgeting' is an alternative name for flexed/flexible budgets (q.v.), although with wider implications. Workload budgeting could be used in future to determine the funding levels of units and of districts. In other words, workload budgeting could provide a basis for the funding of health authorities on the basis of actual work done, in place of or supplementing the present RAWP (q.v.) funding allocation system. The agreed, budgeted fixed costs (q.v.) of units and districts would be guaranteed by regions, on a year-by-year basis, but the variable costs (q.v.) would be funded only on the evidence of the volume of patient treatment delivered. This system could lead to increased competition to attract patients (if funding for cross-boundary patients followed immediately), and to a major reduction in the NHS's waiting lists. Equally, it could lead to lowered standards of treatment unless good quality assurance monitoring systems were introduced simultaneously.

**Zero-base budgeting (ZBB).** 'Zero-base budgeting' is the opposite of the traditional public sector incremental budgeting (q.v.), where debate is largely about marginal increases or decreases in the existing level of budget and real terms (q.v.) resources. Under strict ZBB the formal presumption is that all activities and budgets of every manager should have to be documented, explained and justified every year in order to obtain a renewed budget allocation.

In practice, this does not seem appropriate in an organization such as the NHS in which most activities are essential for maintaining health standards. On the other hand, the philosophy, or state of mind, represented by ZBB may well be helpful to managers and especially general managers. That is, the need for expenditure on particular resources or services should always be open to challenge. Priorities change, social and human needs and the solutions to problems change through time. The NHS must be dynamic, not static.

# Appendix

Since this book started typesetting, a few new publications of high relevance have been announced. *DRGs and Health Care – the management of case mix* by M. Bardsley, J. Coles and L. Jenkins, King Edward's Hospital Fund (1987) should become the definitive UK reference on DRGs (see Chapter 9). The CIPFA and HFMA (see Glossary) have been working on a major NHS management information database. The first volume of hard copy output from this is now published (including coverage of financial resources, activity, morbidity, manpower, regional strategic plans and related matters), and Volume 2 (a statistical backup to the first volume) may indeed have been published by the time this book is printed and in circulation.

Turning to the NHS initiative in Resource Management (Chapter 8), press comment on progress to date was included in the *Health Service Journal* of 30 July 1987 (870–1), and it has been announced that issue no. 7 of the *NHS Management Bulletin* (which may well be in print before this book) will include a detailed progress report on the several resource management projects.

Among recent Departmental publications, HC(87)9 gives support for the new NHS audit manual and standards; while DA(87)29 announced the revaluation of the NHS estate and the provision of rental equivalents. The latter are of course important for the better control of NHS capital resources (Chapter 8).

# Index